JN110446

松森靖夫
Yasuo Matsumori 監修

Steve Mills
英文監修

素朴な「？」がよくわかる！

新版 英語対訳で読む科学の疑問

JIPPI
Compact

実業之日本社

装幀●杉本欣右
イラスト●笹森　識
日本文執筆●中村英良＋森井美紀
DTP・編集●スタジオスパーク

　私たちの身の周りには、さまざまな『疑問』が満ちあふれています。その中には、知っているようで本当は知らないこと、答えられそうで実はなかなかうまく答えられないものがあります。

　たとえば、「宇宙の果ては、どうなっているの？」、「空はなぜ、青いの？」、「動物にはなぜ、雄と雌がいるの？」、「人間はどうして、必ず死ぬの？」、「携帯電話はなぜ、つながるの？」……などなど。

　本書では、そうした素朴だけれど、答えに窮するようないろいろな疑問について、科学の眼を通して解明しています。しかも、それを平易な日本語と中学レベルのやさしい英語でダブル解説するという、初めての試みの本です。

　宇宙や地球に関すること、私たち人間を含めた生き物に対すること、また、私たちの体についてのこと、そのほか、私たちの生活全般にかかわることなど、79項目を取り上げました。

　構成については、「問」に対する「答」というスタイルにし、答えに関して諸説あるものについては、代表的なもの、最新の学説を優先しました。ですから、本書で解説した答えが唯一無二のものではなく、ほかの回答や学説がある場合もあることをお断りしておきます。

　また、英文と日本文の両方に番号を振ってあるので、読者のみなさんが英文を読んでいてわからないところが出てきたときには、対応する日本文がすぐに見つけられるようになっています。

　英語学習には、テーマや内容の面白さがないと、なかなか長続きしないものです。その意味からも、興味が尽きない本書の「科学の疑問」を読みながら、知らず知らずのうちに英語に強くなっていただければ、これに過ぎる喜びはありません。

　なお、本書作成にあたっては、山梨大学の理科のプロフェッショナルである松森靖夫先生、およびスティーブ・ミルズ氏の監修を仰ぎました。この場を借りて、厚くお礼申し上げます。

There are various questions which we can not understand around us. Some of them are the questions which we think we understand but actually we do not understand and which we think we can answer but actually we can not answer well.

Some examples of them are "What is there at the end of the universe?", "Why does the sky look blue?", "Why do animals have two sexes, male and female?", "Why must all human beings die?", "How are cell-phones connected?", and so on.

Such questions, which are simple but we can not answer well, are scientifically clarified in this book. Furthermore, this is the first book to answer the questions both in simple Japanese and in simple English, which even junior high school students may understand.

79 topics about universe, the earth, creatures including human beings, our body, and many things in our daily life are picked up.

This book adopts the questions and answers style. When a question has various believable answers, the typical and latest theory is introduced. Therefore note that the answer introduced in this book is not the only one and some questions have many other answers and theories.

Every Japanese and English sentence is numbered in this book. Therefore when you have difficulty in reading the English sentences, you can find their Japanese translation in no time.

You may give up studying English easily if the textbook does not have interesting subjects and contents. From this point of view, it would be more than happy if you can brush up your English unconsciously by reading the very interesting science questions and answers in this book.

In closing, in the course of making this book, Professor Matsumori Yasuo of University of Yamanashi, the specialist in science supervised the Japanese part and Mr. Steve Mills supervised the English part of this book. I would like to express special thanks to them all.

Chapter 1

....

Questions about the universe/ 宇宙の疑問

Chapter 2

....

Questions about the earth/ 地球の疑問

Questions about creatures / 生き物の疑問

Chapter 4

Questions about human body/ 人間の体の疑問

CONTENTS / 目次

Questions about the universe

第 1 章

宇宙の疑問

When and how
the universe was born?

①Various hypotheses have been proposed to
　　　　　ハイポセシーズ
　　　　さまざまな　仮説　　　　　　　　　　　　～が提案された

explain how the universe was born. ②The
　　　　どのように宇宙ができたか

most popular among them is the Big Bang theory.
　　　　　　　　　　　　　　　　　ビッグバン理論

③According to this theory, the universe was originally an
　～によると

extremely small dot, which was red hot and high dense.
極端に小さな点　　　　　　　　　　　　灼熱の　　　　高密度な

④This theory says that the dot began to get bigger and
　　　　　　　　　　　　　　　　　　　　　　　　どんどん拡張する

bigger very rapidly in time and space as if it had
　　　　　　　　　　　　　時空において

blown up, and then the universe was born.
あたかも爆発したかのように

⑤In many different ways, scientists are studying about
　　いろいろな方法で

when the universe was born. ⑥An electromagnetic wave
いつ宇宙ができたのか　　　　　　　　電磁気の波 (→電磁波)

named CMB (cosmic microwave background radiation)
　　　　宇宙のマイクロ波の背景放射 (→宇宙マイクロ波背景放射)

played an important part in their studies. ⑦CMB is a very
重要な役割を果たした

old electromagnetic wave like a fossil sent out soon after
　　　　　　　　　　　　　　化石のような　放出された

the universe was born and it reaches the earth from all

around the space even today.

⑧ NASA (National Aeronautics and Space Administration)
　　　米航空宇宙局(←国家の航空と宇宙の組織)

launched a microwave observatory satellite to
　～を打ち上げた　マイクロ波を観測する衛星　　　　　　～を観測するために

monitor CMB. ⑨The results of analysis show that the
　　　　　　　　　　　～の分析結果

universe wasborn about 13.7 billion years ago. (see p.22)
　　　　　　　　137億年前

(see p.22)

問1　宇宙はいつ、どのようにしてできたの？

答　①宇宙の成立については、さまざまな仮説が、立てられてきました。②その中で現在一番広く受け入れられているのが「ビッグバン理論」です。

③このビッグバン理論では、宇宙の始まりはとてつもなく高温、高密度で限りなく小さい、点のようなかたまりです。④これがあたかも爆発したかのように急激に時間と空間の拡張を始め、宇宙が生まれたとされています。

⑤宇宙誕生の時期についてもさまざまな研究がなされています。⑥この研究に貢献したのはCMB（宇宙マイクロ波背景放射）という電磁波でした。⑦CMBは宇宙が誕生して間もない頃に出された化石のような電磁波であり、現在でも宇宙のあらゆる方向から地球に届いています。

⑧NASA（米航空宇宙局）はCMBを観測するために、マイクロ波観測衛星を打ち上げました。⑨その結果の解析から、宇宙は約137億年前に生まれたとされています。

Q 2 What is there at the end of the universe?

①First of all, how far into space can we see ? ②It
　　　　　　　どのくらい遠く
is said that the universe was born around 13.7
～といわれている
billion years ago. ③Since the distance that light travels in a
　　　　　　　　　　　　距離　　　　　　光　　進む
year is called a light year, the light the earth catches now
　　　　　　　光年
was given off 13.7 billion years ago by stars 13.7 billion
放たれた　　　　　　　　　　　　　　　　　　　137億光年離れた
light years away. ④Therefore we should be able to see 13.7
　　　　　　　　　　だから　　　　　　～できるはずだ
billion light years away.

⑤In 1929, an American astronomer, Edwin Hubble, found
　　　　　　アメリカ人天文学者　　　　　エドウィン・ハッブル　発見した
that the universe is continuing to expand. ⑥He said that all
　　　　　　　　　　　　大きくなり続けている
the stars in the universe are moving away from the earth,
　　　　　　　　　　　　　　　　　　～から遠ざかって動いている
and that the further a star is from the earth, the faster it
　　　　　　　遠ざかれば遠ざかるほど（速くなる）
moves.

⑦To sum up, if we think of the end of the universe as the
　要するに　　　　　　　～を－と考える 宇宙の果て
furthest point we can see, it is 13.7 billion light years away
最も遠い地点
now and it is still extending. ⑧When we think of the end of
the universe as the limit of space, not as the furthest point
　　　　　　　　　　空間における限界

14

we can see, we can not even find yet whether there is an
　　　　　　　　　　　　　　　　　　　～であるかどうか
end to it or not.

問2　宇宙の果てはどうなっているの？

答 ①まず、宇宙はどこまで見えるかを考えてみましょう。②宇宙が誕生したのは約137億年前といわれています。③光が1年間に進む距離を1光年といいますので、137億光年離れた星が137億年前に発した光が、今やっと地球に届いていることになります。④現在の地球からどこまで見渡せるかを考えると、137億光年の彼方まで、ということになります。

⑤1929年には、アメリカのエドウィン・ハッブルという学者が、宇宙は膨張し続けていることを発見しました。⑥銀河のすべての星が地球から遠ざかるように動き、その速度は地球からその星までの距離に比例して速くなるというのです。

⑦つまり、宇宙の果てが「見える限界」と考えると、現在は137億光年彼方であり、刻々と広がり続けていることになります。⑧見える限界ではなく、空間としての限界ということになると、今のところ宇宙の果てが存在しているかどうかさえ、わかっていません。

Q3 Is there any planet human beings can live on in space?

①A planet on which human beings can live must
〔人類が住むことのできる惑星〕
meet certain conditions, for example it must have
〔～にかなう〕 〔条件〕
water, it must have a temperature similar to that of the earth, it
〔地球と似た気温〕
must be made up of rock and metal, and so on. ②In the solar
〔～からできている〕 〔太陽系で〕
system Mars meets some of these conditions. ③However, the
〔火星〕
average temperature on Mars is low, around minus 60 degrees
〔平均気温〕 〔摂氏マイナス60度〕
Celsius, and about more than 90 percent of its atmosphere
〔大気〕
consists of carbon dioxide. ④Therefore human beings can not
〔～からなる〕 〔二酸化炭素〕
live on Mars.

⑤Then, how about outside this solar system? ⑥The earth
〔～の外側〕
is a planet moving around the sun, a fixed star. ⑦Apart
〔恒星〕 〔～以外にも〕
from the sun, there are countless fixed stars which give off
〔無数の〕 〔～を放つ〕
light on their own out there in the universe. ⑧There
〔宇宙全体の中に〕
could be some planets around these fixed stars which have

a similer environment to that of the earth.
〔地球と似た環境〕
⑨For example, there is a planet named Gliese 581 d, which
〔グリーゼ581d〕

moves around a fixed star, Gliese 581, 20.4 light-years away
〈～から20.4光年離れた〉
from the solar system. ⑩Based on the nature of Gliese 581,
〈性質〉
the Sun-like star, and the distance between Gliese 581 and
〈距離〉
Gliese 581d, it appears that there may be some water on
〈～のようだ〉
Gliese 581d which would be essential for some organisms
〈～が～するのに欠くことのできない〉〈生物〉
to live there.

問3　宇宙に人間が住める星はあるの？

答 ①人間が住める星には、水がある、気温が地球に近い、岩石や金属などでできているなど、いくつかの条件があります。②太陽系でこの条件に近い星は火星です。③しかし、平均気温がマイナス60度前後と低く、大気の90パーセント以上は二酸化炭素です。④これでは、人間が住めそうにもありません。⑤では、太陽系以外ではどうでしょうか？　⑥地球は、恒星である太陽の周りを回っている惑星です。⑦広い宇宙には、太陽のほかにも、自ら光を放つ星である恒星が無数に存在します。⑧その周りには、地球と同じような環境の惑星が存在する可能性は十分にあります。

⑨たとえば、太陽系から20.4光年離れたグリーゼ581という名前の恒星の周りを回る惑星、グリーゼ581dです。⑩太陽にあたるグリーゼ581の性質や、そこからの距離で、グリーゼ581dには生命の生存に欠かせない水があると考えられています。

Why is the sun burning all the time?

①Like the other fixed stars, the sun also gives off
　　　　　　　　　恒星　　　　　　　　　　　　　　　　　～を放つ

large amounts of energy and light by a nuclear
大量の～

fusion reaction of hydrogen to form helium. ②The sun is
～が—を形成する核融合反応　水素　　　　　　ヘリウム

about 109 times the diameter of the earth and it is thought
　　　109倍　　　　直径　　　　　　　　　　　　　　　　～だと考えられる

that about 90 percent of the mass of the sun is hydrogen.
　　　　　　　　　　　　　　質量

③Scientists say that as much as about 700 million tons of
　　　　　　　　　　～もの量　　　　　　7億トン

hydrogen is used for the nuclear fusion reaction per second
　　　　　　　　　　　　　　　　　　　　　　　　　　毎秒

at the center of the sun.

④However, the sun will not go on shining forever like
　　　　　　　　　　　　　　輝き続ける

today. ⑤When there is little hydrogen left and helium
　　　　　　　　　　　　残された水素が少ない

comes to the center of the sun, the nuclear fusion reaction

of hydrogen outside speeds up and expands outward. ⑥It is
　　　　　　　　　加速する　　　　外側に広がる

called a red giant. ⑦After that, those gases flow out and it
　　　赤色巨星　　　ドゥオーフ　　　　　　　　　流出する

becomes a white dwarf, which has no nuclear fusion
　　　　　白色矮星

reactions, and it then takes billions of years to become cold.
　　　　　　　　　　　　　　　数十億年

⑧The sun, which is thought will exist for around 10 billion
　　　　　　　　　　　　　　　存続する　　　　　　　100億年

years, is now about <u>4.7 billion years old.</u> ⑨Therefore the
　　　　　　　　　　　47億歳

sun will shine <u>as it does today</u> for <u>billions of years more.</u>
　　　　　　　　今日のように　　　　　あと数十億年間

(see p.23)

問4　太陽はどうして、ずっと燃えているの？

答 ①太陽もほかの恒星と同じように、水素がヘリウムに変化する核融合反応によって大量のエネルギーを発生し、光を放っています。②直径が地球の約109倍もある巨大な太陽ですが、その質量の90パーセント程度が水素だと考えられています。③中心では、毎秒約7億トンもの水素が核融合反応によって消費されているといわれています。

④しかし、太陽はずっと今のように輝き続けるわけではありません。⑤水素が残り少なくなると、ヘリウムが中心に集まり、その外側にある水素の核融合が加速して外側に広がっていきます。⑥これが赤色巨星です。⑦その後、ガスが流出して核融合反応が起こらない白色矮星(わいせい)となり、数十億年かけて冷えていきます。

⑧寿命100億年前後と考えられている太陽は、現在約47億歳です。⑨そのため、あと数十億年は、今の状態で輝き続けることでしょう。

Why is the earth

moving around the sun?

①Everything in this universe has the power to
<u>引きつける力</u>
<u>pull all other things</u>, and <u>the things which has a</u>
<u>ほかのあらゆるもの</u>　<u>より質量が大きいものほど</u>
<u>larger mass</u> have stronger power. ②This is called <u>the</u>

<u>universal gravitation</u>.
万有引力
③<u>Put a strong magnet</u> on the ground and <u>roll an iron ball</u>
<u>強力な磁石</u>　<u>～を転がす 鉄の玉</u>
near the magnet. ④The iron ball will not go straight

because the strong magnet will pull it. ⑤The iron ball will

<u>change direction a little</u> or <u>go straight to</u> the magnet
<u>少し方向を変える</u>　<u>まっすぐ～へ向かう</u>
<u>depending on</u> <u>the strength of</u> the magnet and <u>the distance</u>
<u>～しだいで</u>　<u>～の強さ</u>　<u>～の間の距離</u>
between these two things.

⑥The iron ball <u>may</u> <u>move around</u> the magnet <u>under certain</u>
<u>～かもしれない ～の周りを回る</u>　<u>ある特定の条件のもとでは</u>
conditions, <u>such as</u> <u>the weight of</u> the iron ball, <u>its speed</u> and
<u>たとえば</u>　<u>～の重量</u>　<u>その速度</u>
the strength of the magnet. ⑦<u>Planets</u> such as the earth and
<u>惑星</u>
others in <u>the solar system</u> can be thought of <u>in this way</u>.
<u>太陽系</u>　<u>このように</u>
⑧The earth moves around the sun <u>because of</u> the
<u>～のために</u>
<u>gravitational pull of</u> the sun and the <u>inertia</u> which the earth
<u>～の引力</u>　<u>慣性</u>

itself has: <u>a property that keeps itself moving.</u>
　　　　　　　　自らを動かし続ける特性

問5　地球は太陽の周りを、どうして回っているの？

答　①この宇宙では、どんなものにも、ほかのものを引きつける力があり、その力は質量が大きくなるほど、大きなものになります。②これが万有引力です。

③強力な磁石を置き、その近くで鉄の玉を転がすとします。④鉄の玉は磁石の方向に引っ張られ、まっすぐに転がらないでしょう。⑤磁石の強さや鉄の玉と磁石の距離によって、方向を変えて転がっていってしまったり、そのまま磁石に引き寄せられたりします。

⑥鉄の玉の重量と、磁石の強さ、転がした速度によって、磁石の周りを回る動きを見せる場合もあります。⑦これが地球などの惑星と考えていいでしょう。

⑧地球は、地球自体が持つ慣性、つまり動き続けようとする性質と、太陽の引力によって公転しているのです。

宇宙は 137 億年前、爆発（ビッグバン）によって生まれた

The universe was born 13.7 billion years ago by an explosion called the Big Bang.

宇宙の初期のころ
The early stages of the universe

宇宙の初期は高温、高密度な一点だったと考えられている。

The universe in the early stage is thought to have been a red-hot and high-density dot.

ビッグバン
The Big Bang

小さな点だった初期宇宙が、あたかも爆発のように大きく膨張し始めた。

The early universe as a dot began to extend as if it had blown up.

宇宙の果ては 137 億光年の彼方

The end of the universe is 13.7 billion light years away.

137 億年前（宇宙の誕生時）に、137 億光年の彼方で発生した光などの電磁波が、現在の地球に届いている。

Electromagnetic waves such as light given off 13.7 billion years ago, at birth of the universe, 13.7 billion light years away reach the earth now.

地球から 137 億光年の距離
13.7 billion light years away from the earth

まだ地球に届いていない
Not reached earth yet

光や電磁波 / Light and electromagnetic waves

現在見える領域
Visible area at present

宇宙の果て
The end of the universe

太陽はやがて燃え尽きる
The sun will burn out some day

現在の太陽
Today's sun

赤色巨星
Red giant

水素が残り少なくなると、外側にある水素の核融合が加速して外側に広がる
When there is little hydrogen left, the nuclear fusion reaction of hydrogen outside speeds up and expands outward.

ガスを放出する
Giving off gases

中心は自らの重力で収縮し、外側を覆うガスは離れていく
The center of it contracts by its own gravity and the gases covering it flow out.

白色矮星
White dwarf

外側のガスがなくなり、地球ほどの大きさになった中心部が白色矮星となる
The gases which covered it flow out and the center of it becomes as small as the earth and a white dwarf.

Q6   **Why is the earth rotating?**

①Gases, dust and small planets were moving
塵   小さな惑星

around like "an eddying current" when the sun
渦潮

was born. ②Since the gases, the dust and the small planets
～して

grew bigger as they continued to run into one after another,
次々に衝突する

the planets of the solar system, including the earth, were
太陽系

born.

③When two balls run into each other, they sometimes

rotate. ④This happens when the two balls do not collide,
回転する   正面同士の衝突ではなく

head-on, but just brush each other. ⑤The earth came to
かすめる   ～するようになる

rotate one time in about 23 hours 56 minutes 4.06 seconds
1度回転する   23時間56分4.06秒

as it does today after continuing to run into other planets
現在そうするように

and so on again and again.
何度も何度も

⑥A rotating ball will stop after a while because of the
しばらくすると

friction between the ball and the ground. ⑦However, the
～の間の摩擦 (抵抗)

earth floating in the universe, which is almost a vacuum,
ほぼ真空の

has no friction to stop it from rotating. ⑧Therefore the
～が—するのを妨げる

earth keeps rotating as long as there is no collision with
～しない限り   ～の衝突

great force, such as a planet. ⑨There are in fact some forces
<u>大きな力</u>　　　　　　　　　　　<u>実際には</u>

which <u>impede</u> the rotation of the earth such as the friction
　　　<u>妨げる</u>

between the tides and the sea bottom among other things.
<u>潮の干満と海底との間の</u>

⑩As a result, the rotation of the earth slows down about
　<u>そのため</u>

one over one hundred thousand seconds every year.
<u>10万分の1秒</u>

問6　　**地球はなぜ、自転しているの？**

答　①太陽が誕生したとき、ガスや塵、小さな惑星が渦を巻いて回っていました。②それらが衝突を繰り返しながら大きくなり、地球をはじめとする太陽系の惑星が生まれました。③二つのボールがぶつかると、回転することがあります。④真正面からぶつからず、中心からはずれてかすったような場合です。⑤地球も、惑星などとの衝突を繰り返すうちに、現在のように約23時間56分4.06秒周期で自転するようになりました。⑥ボールは回転しても、地面に接している面で抵抗があるため、やがて止まってしまいます。⑦ところが、真空にほぼ近い宇宙に浮かぶ地球に対しては、回転を妨げる抵抗がありません。⑧そのため、惑星との衝突といった大きな力が加わらない限り、回転し続けます。⑨ただし、地球にも、潮の干満と海底との摩擦など、自転を妨げる力が働いています。⑩そのため、1年間に約10万分の1秒ずつ自転速度が遅くなっています。

Q 7 Why are the earth, the sun, and the moon spheres?

①Almost all the stars, including the earth, the
ほとんどすべての〜　　　〜を含めて
sun, and the moon, are spherical in shape. ②This
形が球の
is the result of gravity.
〜の結果　　重力
③Various substances floating in the universe are put
さまざまな　物質　　宇宙に浮かんでいる　　　集められ
together by gravity and a star is born. ④In any case, gravity
いかなる場合でも
pulls things toward its center. ⑤If a star had the shape of a
もし〜なら—だろう
cube, its vertexes would have weaker gravity as they are far
立方体　頂角　　　　　　より弱い　　　〜なので
from its center and the part around its center would have
stronger gravity as it is near its center. ⑥In a sphere, the
より強い　　　　　　　　　　　　　　　　　スフィア
　　　　　　　　　　　　　　　　　　　　　　球
distance between its center and any points on its surface is
〜と—の距離　　　　　　　　　いかなる点　　　表面
the same. ⑦Therefore any points on its surface have the
same gravity. ⑧Some newborn stars are not spherical in
生まれたばかりの
shape, but even such stars gradually become spheres
〜でさえ　　　しだいに
because of gravity in the course of time. ⑨Some minor
時間がたつにつれて　　　　　小惑星
planets with low mass do not become perfect balls because
小さい質量
of their weak gravity. ⑩The minor planet named Toutatis,
トータティス

26

which came <u>dangerously near</u> to the earth in November
　　　　　危険なくらい近くに
2008, is only 4.9 km long even at its <u>longest point</u>. ⑪It was
　　　　　　　　　　　　　　　　　　　　最も長い部分でも
oval in shape, <u>resembling</u> the shape of two <u>combined stars</u>,
楕円形の　　　　　～に似ている　　　　　　　　合体した2つの星
by observed through a <u>telescope</u>. (see p.34)
　　　　　　　　　　　　望遠鏡

問7　　　　**なぜ、地球も太陽も月も丸いの？**
・・・・・・・・・・・・・・・・・・・・・・・・・・・・

答　①地球、太陽、月に限らず、ほとんどの星は球の形をし
ています。②これは、重力によるものです。
③重力によって宇宙をさまようさまざまな物質が集まり、星が
生まれます。④重力は、常に中心にむかって働きます。⑤仮に
星が立方体だとすると、中心から遠い角の部分は重力が弱くな
り、中心に近い部分の重力が大きくなります。⑥球では、中心
から表面のあらゆる地点までの距離が同じです。⑦そのため、
表面のどの地点にも同じように重力が働きます。⑧生まれたば
かりの星は球体でないこともありますが、時間がたつにつれ、
重力によって球体になっていくのです。
⑨質量が小さい小惑星などの中には、重力が小さいために球体
になりきれないものもあります。⑩2008 年 11 月に地球に異
常接近した小惑星トータティスは、一番長い部分でも 4．9 キ
ロメートルしかありません。⑪望遠鏡がとらえたその姿は、楕
円形に近い、二つの星が合体したようなものでした。

Q 8 Why don't people and things on the other side of the earth fall off even though they are upside-down?

①The word "fall" expresses a movement from
落ちる ～を表す 上から下への動き
top to bottom. ②The South Pole of the earth is at
南極
the bottom of a model world globe, under which there is a
～の最下部 地球儀 その下には
pedestal. ③Even if you try to put a small doll on the South
台座 ～だとしても
Pole of a model world globe, it will fall to the pedestal.

④However, this is the case of a model world globe, not the
～の場合
case of the real globe. ⑤This is why there is no concept of
本当の地球 それは～だからだ ～という概念がない
top and bottom in space.

⑥Now, let us think about what the word "bottom" means.

⑦You will soon find that we use "bottom" to express "the

direction toward the ground". ⑧To be exact, the direction
地面の方向 正確にいうと 重力が～する方向
of gravity to pull things is the "bottom". ⑨Anywhere on
どこでも
the earth, gravity pulls things toward the center of the
～の中心付近
earth.

⑩"Falling" means a movement of things toward the center
～にむかうものの動き

of the earth by the pull of gravity. ⑪In other words,
言い換えると
everything falls toward the center of the earth even at the

South Pole though it is at the bottom of the world globe.

問8　なぜ、地球の反対側の人や物は上下逆さ
なのに落ちないの？

答　①私たちにとって、「落ちる」というのは、上から下に落ちることを意味します。②地球儀を見ると、南極は一番下のほうにあり、その下には地球儀を置いてある台座があります。③地球儀の南極に小さな人形を置こうとしても、下の台座のほうに落ちてしまうでしょう。

④しかし、これは机に置かれた地球儀であって、本物の地球となると話が違ってきます。⑤宇宙には、上も下もないからです。⑥ここで、「下」とは何なのか考えてみましょう。⑦「下」というのは「地面がある方向」であることに気づくでしょう。⑧ちょっと難しい言い方をすれば、重力が働く方向が「下」です。⑨地球上のどこでも、重力は地球の中心付近にむかって働いています。⑩「落ちる」とは、重力に引っぱられ地球の中心の方向にむかって移動することです。⑪つまり、地球儀の下にある南極であっても、ものは地球の中心にむかって落ちるのです。

Q 9 Why does the moon change its shape?

①The moon is the nearest star to the earth of all
最も～の近くにある星
the stars in solar system and it is the only satellite
～の唯一の衛星
of the earth, which goes around it. ②The moon itself does

not give off light, but just seems to shine. ③The surface of
～を放つ　　　輝いているように見えるだけ　　～の表面
the moon is covered with rocks which reflect sunlight in
～で覆われている　　　　　　反射する　太陽の光
different directions and some of the light reaches the earth.
さまざまな方向に
④That is why the moon is not as bright as the sun.
そういうわけで　　　　　～ほど－ない
⑤Sunlight is parallel and strong. ⑥Therefore only half of
平行な
the surface of the moon reflects sunlight.

⑦It takes about four weeks for the moon to go around the
～が－するのに－かかる
earth one time. ⑧While it goes around, the positions of the
～の位置
sun, the earth, and the moon change. ⑨According to the
～に従って
positions, the moon seen from the earth changes its shape
地球から見られた～　　　その形を変える
from new moon to half moon, and to full moon.
新月　　　　　半月　　　　　満月
⑩On the day when the moon and the sun are in the same
～から見て同じ方角に
direction seen from the earth, the part of the moon lit by
～の部分　　　　　太陽に照らされた～
the sun can not be seen from the earth. ⑪In this case, only
～から見られることができない　　　このような場合において

30

the outline of the moon or a very young moon can be seen.
〜の輪郭だけ　　　　　　　　　　　とても細い月
⑫This is called a new moon.

⑬The moon moves about 180 degrees in two weeks and, in
　　　　　　　　　　　　180度　　　　　2週間で
this case, only the part of the moon lit by the sun can be

seen from the earth. ⑭This is called a full moon. (see p.35)

問9　　なぜ、月の形は変化するの？

答 ①月は太陽系の中でもっとも地球に近く、地球の周りを回っている唯一の衛星です。②月は自らが光っているのではなく、光っているように見えるだけです。③でこぼこした岩石で覆(おお)われた表面が太陽の光を乱反射し、その一部が地球に届くのです。④月が太陽ほど明るくないのは、このためです。
⑤太陽光は、平行で強い光です。⑥そのため、太陽の光を受けて光って見えるのは、月の半分だけです。
⑦月は地球の周りを約4週間かけて1回りします。⑧その間に、太陽、地球、月の位置関係は変わります。⑨この位置関係の変化により、地球から見た月は新月、半月、満月と形を変えるのです。
⑩地球から見て月と太陽が同じ方向にある日は、太陽光が当たっている部分が見えません。⑪地球からは月の輪郭(りんかく)、あるいはごく細い月がわずかに見えるだけです。⑫これが「新月(しんげつ)」です。
⑬2週間ほどたつと月は約180度移動し、地球からは月の太陽が当たっている部分しか見えなくなります。⑬これが満月です。

Q 10 Why does the moon keep up with us when we are walking?

①Suppose that you are walking along the street
〜だと想像しよう

at night, and that, by the roadside, there is a
道ばたに

telephone pole 10 meters ahead and an iron tower one
電柱　　　　10メートル前方に　　　　　　鉄塔

kilometer ahead. ②When you walk 10 meters, you are just
〜のちょうど横にいる

beside the telephone pole. ③At that time, the iron tower is

990 meters ahead of you and it looks almost like what you
〜とほぼ同じに見える　見たもの

saw 10 meters behind. ④When you are moving, you feel
10メートル後方で

that distant things do not change their position as much as
遠くのもの　　　〜ほど一しない　位置を変える

nearby things.
近くのもの

⑤It is as far as 380 thousand kilometers from the earth to
〜も　　　380,000キロメートル

the moon. ⑥Even if you move a few kilometers, you do not
〜だとしても　　　　　　　　　まったく〜しない

feel that the position of the moon you see changes at all.
見える月の位置

⑦In daily life, you do not feel that the position of a distant

thing changes (a) when both you and the thing are moving

at the same speed or (b) when both you and the thing are
同じ速度で

standing still. ⑧Since you supposed that you were walking
静止している　　　〜なので

32

along the street at night, it is clear that (b) is not the case
　　　　　　　　　　　　　　　　　~なのは明らかだ　　~がここでの状況ではない

here. ⑨Therefore you get it wrong and think that the moon
　　　　　　　　　　　間違える

keeps up with you.
~についてくる

問10　　歩いていると、なぜ月はついてくるの？

答　①たとえば、夜道を歩いていて 10 メートル前方の道路わきに電柱があり、1 キロ前方に鉄塔があったとします。②10メートル進むと、あなたは電柱の真横にたどり着きます。③一方鉄塔は、990 メートル前方にあり、10 メートル前から見たのとほとんど変わっていないでしょう。④動いているあなたから見ると、遠くのものは近くのものに比べて位置変化が少なく感じられるのです。

⑤地球から月までの距離は 380,000 キロメートルもあります。⑥2 キロや 3 キロ移動したところで、あなたから見た月の位置はまったく変わりません。

⑦日常生活で、あなたと離れたものとの位置関係が変わらないのは、(a) 両方とも同じ速度で移動しているか、(b) 両方とも静止しているかのどちらかです。⑧あなたは夜道を歩いているので、(b) ではないことは明らかです。⑨そのため、月が同じように動いていると錯覚してしまうのです。

大きな天体が球形なのは、表面の重力が均等に働くから

Big stars are spherical in shape because any points on their surface have the same gravity.

球
Sphere

立方体
Cube

表面のどの場所でも、重力は均等に働く。
Any points on their surface have the same gravity.

中心に近いほど、大きな重力が働く。
The nearer the point comes to its center, the stronger gravity becomes.

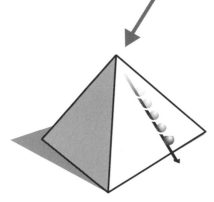

ものは重力が小さいところから大きいところへ移動しようとする。
Everything is always likely to move toward the point having strong gravity from the point having weak gravity.

▼

その結果、全体に重力が均等な球形になる。
Therefore it became a sphere, which has the same gravity at any points on its surface.

月で光が当たっている部分は、地球との位置関係に よって見え方が変わる

The part of the moon lit by the sun changes its shape according to the positions of the moon and the earth when we see from the earth.

上弦
First quarter

満月
Full moon

太陽からの光
Sunlight

新月
New moon

下弦
Last quarter

新月
New moon

半月
Half moon

太陽からの光
Sunlight

満月
Full moon

Why do shooting stars fall?

①Shooting stars are called "stars", but in fact
流れ星　　　　　　　　　　　　　　実際には
they are not stars. ②They are small dust particles
塵の粒子
floating along the earth's orbital path. ③It is said that the
〜をさまよっている　地球の公転軌道
smallest dust particle is about 0.1 millimeters across and
直径0.1ミリメートル
even the biggest dust particle is only several centimeters

across. ④These dust particles burn up and give off bright
燃える　　　　〜を放つ　明るい光
light after they enter the earth's atmosphere.
地球の大気圏

⑤Most of these dust particles, which could become
流星になるかもしれない〜
shooting stars, were left by comets. ⑥A comet is like a
彗星
mass of ice which has a lot of dust inside it. ⑦When comets
氷の塊　　　　　内部にたくさんの塵を含んだ
are far from the sun, they are frozen hard. ⑧However,
凍りついている
when they come nearer to the sun, they melt little by little
融ける 少しずつ
and leave various substances behind. ⑨The vapor-trail-like
〜をあとに残す さまざまな物質　　　　飛行機雲のような
substances left after a comet passes by are called "dust
残された　　　　　通過する　　　ダストトレイル
trails".

⑩Fine dust particles shower onto the earth when it goes
細かい　　　　〜に降り注ぐ　　　　　　　通り抜ける
through the "dust trail" left along its orbital path. ⑪As a
〜に残された

result, a lot of shooting stars are seen from the earth.
その結果

問11　　流れ星はどうして流れるの？

答　①流れ星は、流星と呼ばれますが星ではありません。②地球の公転軌道にさまよっている小さな塵です。③小さなもので直径0.1ミリメートルくらい、大きなものでも直径数センチメートルだといわれています。④これが地球の大気圏に突入するときに燃え、明るい光を放つのです。

⑤流星のもとになる塵は、主に彗星が残していったものです。⑥彗星は、たくさんの塵を含んだ氷の塊のようなものです。⑦太陽から離れた場所にいるときは凍りついています。⑧太陽に近づくにつれ氷が融け、さまざまな物質を残していきます。⑨彗星が通過したあとに飛行機雲のように残る物質は、ダストトレイルと呼ばれます。

⑩地球が、公転軌道上に残されたダストトレイルの中を通過すると、細かい塵が地球上に降り注ぎます。⑪このとき、地球上からは多くの流星が観測できるのです。

Why do stars shine?

①Of all the stars, the ones which give off light
すべての星の中で　　　　　　　　　　～を放つ

are called fixed stars. ②Fixed stars give off
恒星

energy because of nuclear fusion reactions. ③Nuclear
核融合反応

fusion reactions form four hydrogen atoms into one helium
～で—を形成する　水素原子　　　　　　　　　　ヘリウム原子

atom. ④This type of reaction is also applied to hydrogen
　　　　　　　　　　　　　　　　～にも応用される　　　水素爆弾

bombs and it gives off a great deal of energy.
　　　　　　　　　　　　　非常に大きな～

⑤The sun is one of the fixed stars. ⑥It is said that the
　　　　　　　　　　　　　　　　　　～といわれている

temperature of the corona around the sun is more than one
温度　　　　太陽のまわりのコロナ

million degrees C. ⑦Fixed stars shine because they are
摂氏100万度　　　　　　　　　　　　光る

heated to a high temperature and give off a great deal of
～にまで加熱される

energy such as light and heat energy.
　　～のような　光や熱のエネルギー

⑧Some stars do not give off light. ⑨Examples of these are

the planets going around a fixed star such as Jupiter, Venus,
　　　　　～の周りを回る　　　　　　　　　　木星　　金星

and the earth. ⑩Seen from the earth, these two stars appear
　　　　　　　　～から見られるとき

to shine. ⑪However, these planets do not give off light but
　　　　　　　　　　　　　　　　　～するのではなく—する

just reflect light from the sun, a fixed star.
　　～を反射する

問12　なぜ、星は光るの？

答　①星の中でも自ら光を出している星は、恒星と呼ばれています。②恒星は、核融合によってエネルギーを放出しています。③核融合というのは、4個の水素原子が1個のヘリウム原子になる反応です。④これは水素爆弾に使われている反応で、非常に大きなエネルギーを発生します。

⑤太陽も恒星の一つです。⑥太陽を取り巻くコロナの温度は摂氏100万度以上もあるといわれています。⑦恒星が光るのは、このように核融合によって高温になり、大量の光や熱などのエネルギーを放出しているからです。

⑧自ら光を出さない星もあります。⑨たとえば、木星や金星、地球などのように、恒星の周りを回る惑星です。⑩地球から見ると、これらの2つの星も光り輝いているように見えます。⑪これらの惑星は実際に輝いているわけではなく、恒星である太陽の光を反射しているだけなのです。

太陽系
The solar system

ブラックホール
Black hole

太陽
Sun

隕石
Meteor

水星
Mercury

金星
Venus

地球
Earth

彗星
Comet

火星
Mars

木星
Jupiter

宇宙ロケット
Space rocket

土星
Saturn

天王星
Uranus

人工衛星
Satellite

海王星
Neptune

宇宙
Universe

Chapter 2

Questions about the earth

第2章

地球の疑問

Why does the sky look blue?

①Smoke is often used as a stage effect in a
<u>舞台演出</u>
concert hall. ②When smoke fills the hall, you
<u>コンサート会場</u>　　　　　　<u>～を満たす</u>
can see a spotlight, which you can not see in other
<u>スポットライト</u>　　　　　　　　　　　<u>ほかの方法で</u>
ways, as a line of a color such that you can see a red
<u>線</u>　　　　　<u>～であるように</u>
spotlight as a red line. ③This is a phenomenon called
<u>現象</u>
scattering whereby light hits particles in the air and
<u>散乱</u>　　　　　　　　　<u>～にぶつかる</u>　<u>粒</u>
changes direction. ④By this scattering, light, which you
<u>方向を変える</u>
can not see in other ways, comes to be seen as a color.

⑤The color of a visible light, a kind of electromagnetic
<u>可視光線</u>　　　　　　　　　<u>電磁波</u>
wave, changes according to its wavelength. ⑥Light with a
<u>～によって</u>　　<u>波長</u>　　　　<u>波長が短い光</u>
short wavelength looks blue and light with a longer
wavelength looks yellow or red. ⑦Scattering changes
<u>波長がもっと長い光</u>
according to the wavelength of light and the size of the
<u>大きさ</u>
particles in the air. ⑧Smoke on the stage scatters all the
<u>～を散乱させる</u>
colors of light such as red, blue, and yellow because the
particles of the smoke are big. ⑨Small particles are likely
<u>～しやすい</u>
to scatter blue light, which has a short wavelength.

⑩There are molecules of oxygen and nitrogen in the thick
　　　　　　　　モラキュールズ
　　　　　　　　分子　　　　酸素　　　　　窒素　　　　　　厚い大気の層
layer of atmosphere covering the earth and they scatter
　　　　　　　　　　　　〜を覆っている—
sunlight. ⑪They are likely to scatter blue light but do not
太陽の光
scatter much red and yellow light because the molecules of

gas in the air are small. ⑫The sky looks blue because blue
気体　　　　　　　　　　　　　　　　　　　　〜に見える
light in sunlight is scattered in the air. (see p.54)

問13　空はどうして青いの？

答 ①コンサート会場の演出で、スモークが使われることがあります。②煙が会場に充満すると、それまで見えなかったスポットライトの光が、赤い光は赤い線になってというように、色の線として見えるようになります。③これは、小さな粒にぶつかった光が方向を変える「散乱」と呼ばれる現象です。④散乱によって、それまで見えなかった光が「色」として見えるようになるのです。⑤電磁波である可視光線の色は、その波長によって変わります。⑥波長が短い光は、私たちに青く見え、波長が長くなると黄色や赤に見えます。⑦散乱は、光の波長と散乱する「粒」の大きさに関係します。⑧ステージのスモークが赤、青、黄色、すべての光を散乱するのは、煙の粒が大きいからです。⑨小さな粒だと、波長が短い青い光ほど散乱します。⑩地球をとり囲む厚い大気の層には酸素や窒素の分子があり、これらが太陽の光を散乱します。⑪気体の分子は小さいので、青い光を多く散乱し、赤や黄色の光はほとんど散乱しません。⑫空が青く見えるのは、太陽光の中の青い光が空で散乱しているからなのです。

Q14　Why are sunsets red?

①The atmosphere of the earth is more than 500
　　大気圏
kilometers thick. ②There are big particles such as
　　500キロメートルの厚さ　　　　　　　　　　　粒
water vapor and dust in the low layer of the atmosphere
水蒸気　　　　塵　　　低層
from the surface of the earth to 35 kilometers high. ③It was
地表から高度35キロメートルまでの
mentioned on pp. 42-43 that blue light in sunlight is likely
～で述べられた　　　　　　　　　　　　太陽光　　　～しやすい
to be scattered by small particles such as molecules of
　～によって散乱される　　　　　　　　　　分子
oxygen and nitrogen. ④On the other hand, bigger particles
酸素　　　窒素　　　　一方
such as water vapor and dust scatter red and yellow light.

⑤In the evening, sunlight travels a long distance in the air
　　　　　　　　　　　進む　　長い距離
along the surface of the earth and reaches your eyes. ⑥As
　　　　　　　　　　　　　　　　　～に届く
this happens, blue light is scattered and little of it can reach
これが起きている間に　　　　　　　　　　　それはほとんど～できない
your eyes. ⑦However, sunlight in the evening looks reddish
　　　　　　　　　　　　　　　　　　　　　　赤っぽい
because red light travels through the air with little
　　　　　　　　　　　　　　　　　　　　　ほとんど散乱せずに
scattering.

⑧The sky in the west becomes red when this red light is

scattered by big particles such as water vapor and dust.

⑨This is what red sunsets are. (see p.54)
　　　　夕焼けがそうであるところのもの

問14　夕焼けはなぜ、赤いの？

答 ①地球の大気圏は500キロメートル以上の厚さがあります。②そのうち、地表から高度35キロメートルまでの低層には水蒸気や塵など、大きな粒が多く漂っています。③太陽光の中の青い光は、大気中の酸素や窒素の分子など、小さな粒によって散乱しやすいことは、42〜43ページで説明したとおりです。④一方、水蒸気や塵など比較的大きな粒は、赤や黄色の光を散乱します。

⑤夕方になると、太陽の光は地表に沿うように、長い距離、大気の中を通過して私たちの目に届きます。⑥その間に、青い光は散乱して少なくなってしまいます。⑦一方、赤い光は、ほとんど散乱することなく大気を突き抜けるので、夕方の太陽光は赤っぽく見えます。

⑧この赤っぽい光を、水蒸気や塵など、大きな粒が散乱すると、空が赤く染まったように見えます。⑨これが夕焼けの正体です。

Why is seawater salty?

①There was no sea on the earth four billion years
<u>ago</u>. ②At that time, the earth was extremely hot
40億年前　　　　　　　　　　　　　　　　　　　極端に熱い
and water was held in the atmosphere in a state of vapor.
　　　　　～に含まれていた　大気　　　　　～の状態で　蒸気
③It is thought that the atmosphere contained hydrogen
クローライド　　　　　　　　　　　　　ダイオクサイド　　　　塩化水素
chloride besides water vapor, carbon dioxide, nitrogen, and
　　～のほかに　水蒸気　　　二酸化炭素　　　　窒素
so on.

④After the earth cooled down in the course of time, it
　　　　　　　冷めた　　　　　しばらくして
started raining. ⑤It was the rain of hydrochloric acid, that
　　　　　　　　　　　　　　　　　塩酸　　　　　つまり
is hydrogen chloride in water. ⑥This rain of hydrochloric
水に溶けた塩化水素
acid fell to the ground, dissolved various substances,
　　　～に落ちた　　　　～を溶かした　さまざまな物質
and made pools in hollow places. ⑦This is how seas
　　　　　水たまり　くぼんだ場所
were born.

⑧Newborn seawater was not salty like it is today, but it was
　生まれたばかりの　　　　　　　塩辛い　今日そうであるように
sour because it was hydrogen chloride water. ⑨The
酸っぱい
hydrogen chloride vaporized and fell to the ground as rain
　　　　　　　　　蒸発した
again and again. ⑩During that time, hydrogen chloride
繰り返して
water dissolved a large amount of sodium and magnesium
　　　　　　　　　大量の　　　　　　ナトリウム　　マグネシウム

on the sea bottom and on the ground. ⑪As a result, sodium
　　　　海底　　　　　　　　　　　　　　　　　　　　　塩化ナトリウム
chloride and magnesium chloride were formed in a
　　　　　　　塩化マグネシウム　　　　　生成された
chemical reaction and accumulated in the sea. ⑫This is
化学反応によって　　　　　　～に蓄積された
how the sour seawater of the old days became salty as it is
　　　　　　　　　　　大昔の
today.

問15　海水はなぜ、塩辛いの？

答　①今から40億年以上前、地球に海はありませんでした。
②非常に高温だったため、水分は水蒸気の状態で大気に含まれていました。③当時の大気は、水蒸気、二酸化炭素、窒素などのほかに、塩化水素を含んでいたと考えられています。
④時間がたつにつれて地球の温度が下がると、雨が降るようになりました。⑤雨といっても、水に塩化水素が溶けた塩酸の雨です。⑥塩酸の雨は地表にある物質を溶かしながら流れ、くぼんだ場所にたまりました。⑦これが海の誕生です。
⑧生まれたばかりの海の水は、今のように塩辛くなく、酸っぱい塩酸でした。⑨塩酸は蒸発して、再び雨となり地上に降り注ぐことを繰り返しました。⑩その過程で、塩酸が海底や地表のナトリウムやマグネシウムなどを大量に溶かし出しました。⑪これが化学反応によって塩化ナトリウムや塩化マグネシウムとなり、海に蓄積されていきました。⑫こうして酸っぱかった海の水が、今のように塩辛くなったのです。

Q16 Why is a mountain top colder though it is nearer to the sun?

①It is said that every 100 meters higher you go
〜ごとに   高く登る
the temperature falls by about 0.6 degrees
気温   下がる 〜ずつ   摂氏0.6度
Celsius. ②You must wonder why high places are colder
        〜に違いない なぜ〜なのかと思う
though they are nearer to the sun.
〜なのに

③Even the highest mountain is not more than 9,000 meters
〜でさえ   せいぜい〜足らず
high. ④This distance is nothing compared with the distance
      距離   ないようなもの 〜と比べると
between the sun and the earth, about 150 million
                              1億5000万キロメートル
kilometers. ⑤Therefore the height of mountains has
                        〜の高さ
nothing to do with the differences in temperature.
〜と関係がない

⑥The reason why higher places are colder has something
    〜である理由   〜と関係がある
to do with air convection and air pressure. ⑦At first, the
            空気の対流   気圧
ground is heated by the sun, and then the air near the
        〜によって温められる
ground is heated by the infrared light given off by the
                        赤外線   〜によって放たれる
ground. ⑧Heated air goes up because it is light. ⑨Only this
must make you think that higher places are warmer. ⑩The
〜を一であると考えさせるに違いない
reason why mountain tops are colder is that the air pressure
            山の上

is lower at higher places. ⑪Heated air expands as it goes to
より低い　　　　　　　　　　　膨らむ　　〜するにつれて

higher places, where the air pressure is lower. ⑫An

adiabatic expansion happens as air expands. ⑬It is the
断熱膨張　　　　　　　　　　　〜する過程で

phenomenon by which temperature falls when air expands
現象　　　　それによって〜するところの

rapidly. ⑭Higher places are colder because of this adiabatic
急速に

expansion.

問16　山の上は太陽に近いのに、どうして寒いの？

答　①標高が100メートル高くなるごとに、気温は摂氏約
0.6度下がるといわれています。②「高いほうが太陽に近いの
に、どうして寒くなるの？」と、疑問に思うでしょう。
③高いといっても、一番高い山でも9000メートル以下。④太
陽と地球の距離、約1億5000万キロメートルに比べれば、
この差はごくわずかです。⑤これでは気温に影響しません。
⑥標高が高くなると気温が下がる理由は、空気の対流と気圧に
関係します。⑦まず、太陽の熱によって地面が温められ、地面
から放たれる赤外線によって、地面付近の空気が温められます。
⑧温められた空気は軽くなるため、上昇します。⑨これだけなら、
上に行くに従って気温が上がるはずです。⑩山の上のほうが気
温が低いのは、標高が高くなるに従って気圧が低くなるからで
す。⑪暖かい空気のかたまりは、気圧が低い上空に行くにつれ
て膨らみます。⑫その過程で、断熱膨張という現象が起こります。
⑬気体が急激に膨張すると、温度が下がる現象です。⑭この断
熱膨張によって、高度が上がるにつれ気温が下がるのです。

Q17　How are auroras formed?

①The sun keeps giving off plasma. ②Plasma is a
　　　　　~を放ち続ける　　プラズマ
stream of particles which have a positive or
~の流れ　　粒子　　　　　　　　　　　正または負の電荷
a negative electric charge. ③It is sometimes called the solar
　　　　　　　　　　　　　　　　　　　　　　　　　　　太陽風
wind because it moves like a wind and covers the solar
　　　　　　　　　　　　　　　　　　　~を覆う　太陽系
system.

④The earth is a huge magnetic body and is surrounded by
　　　　　　　　巨大な磁石　　　　　　　~に囲まれている
a magnetic field, whose south pole is around the Arctic
磁場　　　　　　　　　　S極　　　　　　　　　　　北極圏
Zone and whose north pole is around the Antarctic Zone.
　　　　　　　　N極　　　　　　　　南極圏
⑤The earth's magnetic field is stretched widely in the
　　　　　　　　　　　　　　　　　広く引き伸ばされている
opposite direction to the sun by the solar wind. ⑥The sun
~と反対方向に
has a magnetic field, too. ⑦The sun's magnetic field is
strong enough to cover the earth's magnetic field.
　　　~するのに十分な—
⑧Magnetic fields have the property of keeping plasma
　　　　　　　　　　　~する特性　　　~を寄せつけない
away. ⑨However, when the sun's magnetic field touches the
　　　　　　　　　　　　　　　　　　　　　~に接する
earth's magnetic field, plasma enters the earth's magnetic
field and rushes into the earth's Arctic Zone and Antarctic
　　　　　~になだれ込む
Zone along the earth's magnetic field lines with a great deal
　　　　　地球の磁力線　　　　　　　　　　　　大量の~

50

of energy. ⑩At that time, plasma collides with atoms and
衝突する　　　　　　　原子
molecules of oxygen and nitrogen in the upper atmosphere
分子　　　　酸素　　　　窒素　　　　高層大気
and light-emitting phenomena take place. ⑪This is how
　　光を放つ～　　現象　　　起こる
auroras are formed. (see p.55)
オーロラのでき方

問17　　**オーロラはどうやってできるの？**

答　①太陽は、いつもプラズマを放出しています。②プラズ
マとは、正または負の電荷をもった粒子の集まりです。③風の
ように流れて太陽系を覆っていることから、太陽風とも呼ばれ
ています。

④地球は北極付近をＳ極、南極付近をＮ極とする大きな磁石
のかたまりであり、磁場に囲まれています。⑤地球の磁場は、
太陽風の影響で太陽と反対方向に大きく引き伸ばされたような
形をしています。⑥太陽にも磁場があります。⑦これは非常に
強いもので、地球の磁場を覆っています。

⑧磁場はプラズマを寄せつけない性質があります。⑨しかし、
太陽の磁場と地球の磁場が接すると、プラズマは地球の磁場に
入り込み、大きなエネルギーを持ちながら地球の磁力線に沿っ
て北極や南極付近になだれ込みます。⑩このとき、プラズマが
高層大気中の酸素や窒素の原子・分子に衝突して光を放ちます。
⑪これがオーロラです。

Q 18 Does air have weight?

①In daily life we do not feel the weight of air, 日常生活 空気の重さ

but, in fact, it has weight. ②1,000 liters of air at 1 1000リットル

atmosphere weighs about 1.2 kilograms. 1気圧において ～の重さがある 1.2キログラム

③The weight of air, 1.2 kilograms per 1,000 liters, is only a ～につき

thousandth the weight of water, so you may think it is very ～の1000分の1の重さ

light. ④However, you are on the ground, which is at the 地上にいる 底

bottom of a thick layer of air. ⑤Air pressure is put on you 厚い層 空気の圧力 ～にかかる

on the ground just like the heavy water pressure that is put 水圧

on you when you dive into the deep sea. ⑥To be exact, air ～に潜る 深海 正確にいうと

weighs 1 kilogram per square centimeter and 10 tons per 1平方センチに

square meter. ⑦To put it simply, air weighs as much as the 1平方メートルに 簡単にいうと

weight of 10 compact cars per square meter. 小型乗用車

⑧It is not easy to weigh air on the earth. ⑨If you put 1,000 ～の重さを量る 入れる

liters of air at 1 atmosphere in a bag and weigh it, it just

weighs 0 grams. ⑩Since the weight of the air in the bag and

the buoyancy of the air around it are in balance, nobody ボイヤンシー 重力 ～がつり合う

can detect the weight of the air. わかる

問18　空気に重さはあるの？

答 ①私たちの日常生活の中で、空気の重さを感じることはありませんが、空気にも重さがあります。②1気圧の空気の重さは1000リットルで約1.2キログラムです。

③1000リットルで1.2キログラムという空気の重さは水の1000分の1であり、大したことはないと思うかもしれません。④しかし、私たちがいる地上は厚い空気の層である大気の底です。⑤深海に潜るとすごい水圧がかかるように、地上にも空気の圧力がかかっています。⑥それがどのくらいかというと、1平方センチあたり1キロ、1平方メートルで10トン。⑦つまり、1平方メートルあたり小型乗用車10台分にも相当するのです。⑧地球上で空気の重さを量ろうとしても簡単ではありません。⑨1気圧の空気、1000リットルを袋に入れて重さを量っても、0グラムにしかなりません。⑩袋の中の空気の重さと周囲の空気の浮力とつり合ってしまうため、重さがないことになってしまうからです。

空の青も夕焼けの赤も、光の散乱による

The sky looks blue and sunset looks red because light is scattered.

青空
Blue sky

太陽光線
Sun light

酸素や窒素などの分子で青い光が散乱する

Blue light is scattered by molecules of oxygen and nitrogen.

地上からは、散乱した青い光が見える

Scattered blue light can be seen from the ground.

夕焼け
Sunset

青い光が減り、赤っぽくなった太陽光線

Reddish sunlight because of little blue light

途中で青い光が散乱し、少なくなる

Blue light is scattered on its way and a little is left.

太陽光線
Sun light

散乱した赤い光が見える

Scattered red light can be seen.

赤い光が水蒸気や塵で散乱する

Red light is scattered by water vapor and dust.

オーロラとは、地球の地磁気に引き込まれた プラズマによる発光現象のこと

Auroras are formed by light-emitting phenomena with plasma pulled by the earth's geomagnetism.

プラズマ
Plasma

太陽風
The solar wind

南極
The Antarctic

北極
The Arctic

プラズマが大気中の酸素や窒素と衝突し、地上からオーロラとして見える
We can see auroras on the ground because plasma collides with oxygen and nitrogen in the atmosphere.

地磁気
Earth's geomagnetism

Q19 How do earthquakes happen?

①The central part of the earth is called the core
　　〜の中心部分　　　　　　　　　　　　　コア (核)
and the part around it is called the mantle.
　　そのまわりの部分　　　　　　　　　マントル
②Outside the mantle there is a layer of a few tens of
　　　　　　　　　　　　　　　層
kilometers thickness called the crust, covers the surface
数十キロメートルの厚さの〜　　　　地殻　　　　　〜の表面
of the earth.

③The mantle is a layer of rocks from the inner surface
　　　　　　　　　岩石の層　　　　〜の内側の表面から
of the crust to a depth of 2,900 kilometers.
　　　　　　　　深さ2900キロメートルまで
④Although the outermost part of the mantle moves very
　　　　　　最も外側の部分
slightly, the part from 100 to 400 kilometers
きわめてわずかに　〜の深さ100〜400キロメートルの部分
deep of the mantle supposed to be moving slowly because of
　　　　　　　　〜と考えられる　　　　　　　　熱対流によって
the heat convection. ⑤In other word, it seems like that masses
　　　　　　　　　言いかえれば　　　　　　　　　かたまり
of the outer mantle and the crust are floating on the layer
　　　　　　　　　　　　　　　　　　〜に浮いている
moving with the convection.
対流で動いている
⑥These floating parts are called plate. ⑦There are two
　　　　　　　　　　　　　プレート
kinds of plate; continental plates and oceanic plates. ⑧The
　　　　　　大陸プレート　　　　海洋プレート
surface of the earth is covered with more than ten plates.

⑨Scientists think that these plates are moved by the mantle's
　　　　　　　　　　　　　　　　　　　　　　マントルの対流

convection, and that they run into or overlap one another.
　　　　　　　　　　　　　　　～に衝突する　　～に重なる　互いに

⑩When some plates move, a heavily loaded part may give
　　　　　　　　　　　　　大きく負荷のかかった部分　　耐えられなくなる

way, cracking or sliding. ⑪This is how earthquakes happen.
　　　ひび割れる　　ずれる

(see p.66)

問19　地震はどうして起きるの？

答　①地球の中心にはコア（核）と呼ばれる部分があり、その外側にマントルがあります。②さらにその外側には数十キロメートルの厚さの地殻があり、これが地球の表面を覆っています。③マントルは、地殻の下から深さ2900キロメートルまで続く岩石の層です。④最上部はほとんど動きませんが、深さ100〜400キロメートルの部分は、熱によりゆっくりと対流していると考えられています。⑤つまり、対流によって動く層の上に、マントルの最上部と地殻がかたまりとなり、浮いているような状態です。

⑥このかたまりはプレートと呼ばれています。⑦プレートには大陸プレートと海洋プレートがあります。⑧地球の表面は10数枚のプレートで覆われています。⑨これらはマントルの対流により移動し、ぶつかったり重なり合ったりしていると考えられています。⑩そして、プレートが移動して、ある部分に大きな力が加わり、耐えられなくなると、そこがひび割れたり、ずれたりします。⑪これが地震です。

Q20　How were the deserts formed?

①You may think of the deserts as sand areas from
their Japanese name, *sabaku*. ②However, sand
areas are called sandy deserts. There are also many rock
deserts in the world, in which bare rocks are exposed.
③Deserts are formed under environments in which the amount
of evaporation is greater than the rainfall. ④When the natural
factor such as dry air or salt in the ground interrupt the growth
of plants, the topsoil enriched with organic matters is washed
away by the rain and blown away by the wind. ⑤This process
finally makes the barren land where animals and plants can
hardly survive. ⑥This is how the deserts are formed.
⑦The characteristic of a desert climate is the big difference
in the temperature between day and night because it is dry.
⑧The surface temperature of rocks goes up in direct
sunlight during the day and it goes down at night. ⑨In the
course of this change of temperature, broken-up rocks are
blown away or hit each other and become small pieces.

⑩The sand made in this way is piled up to make a sandy
　　　　　　このようにして　　積み重なって〜になる
desert.

問20　　　　　　**砂漠はどうやってできたの？**

答　①「砂漠」というと、砂地だと思いがちです。②しかし、砂に覆われているのは砂砂漠であり、世界的に見て多いのは岩肌がむき出しになった岩石砂漠です。

③砂漠ができる原因となるのは、降水量よりも水の蒸発量が多い環境です。④乾燥や地表の塩分などにより植物が育ちにくくなると、有機物を含んだ表土が流されたり風に飛ばされたりしてなくなります。⑤その結果、さらに動植物が生息しにくい不毛の地と化してしまいます。⑥これが砂漠です。

⑦乾燥しているため、昼夜の気温の差が大きいことが砂漠の気候の特徴です。⑧昼間は直射日光を浴びた岩の表面温度は上昇し、夜になると冷えます。⑨これを繰り返しているうちに、岩はぼろぼろに崩れ、風に飛ばされたり、ぶつかり合ったりして細かくなります。⑩こうしてできた砂が堆積すると、砂砂漠になります。

Q 21 Which is colder, the North Pole or the South Pole?

①You may think the North Pole and the South Pole are
~するかもしれない　北極　　　　　　　　　南極
of the same temperature because they are both polar
　　　　　　　　　　　　　　　~なので　　　　　　　　　極地
areas, but, in fact, the South Pole is colder.

②The South Pole is a continent and has various landform
　　　　　　　　　　　　大陸　　　　　　さまざまな　地形の変化
changes, as is the case with other continents. ③There are
　　　　　~によくあるように
mountains such as the Ellsworth Mountains and the Yamato
山脈　　　　　　　　エルスワース山脈　　　　　　やまと山脈
Mountains. ④The highest mountain is Vinson Massif,
　　　　　　　　　　　　　　　　　　　ヴィンソン・マシフ山
which is 4,892 meters above sea level and higher than the
　　　　　4,892メートル　　　標高
Matterhorn in the Alps.
マッターホルン　　アルプス
⑤The North Pole is a sea covered with ice. ⑥The ice is
　　　　　　　　　　　　　　　~で覆われた
about ten meters thick on average and there are no high
　　　10メートルの厚さ　　平均して
places unlike the South Pole.
　　　~と違って
⑦In general, when you compare temperatures in places on
　一般的に　　　　　　　~を比較する　~の気温
the same latitude, land is likely to be colder than sea
同緯度の　　　　　　陸　　~する傾向がある
and highlands are likely to be colder than lowlands. ⑧The
　　高地　　　　　　　　　　　　　　　低地
reason why the South Pole is colder is that it is land and is
~である理由

higher above sea level. ⑨It is said that the average

temperature at the South Pole is about 20 degrees C
　　　　　　　　　　　　　　　　　　　平均気温

lower than that at the North Pole. ⑩The lowest temperature
～よりも摂氏20度低い　　　　　　　　　　　　　　　　最低気温

measured on earth is minus 93.2 degrees C, recorded at the
～で観測された　　　　　　摂氏マイナス93.2度　　　　～で記録された

East Antarctic Plateau in the South Pole on August 10, 2010.
東南極高原

問21　北極と南極では、どちらが寒いの？

答　①北極と南極はどちらも極地であるため、気温も変らないように思うかもしれませんが、寒いのは南極のほうです。②大陸である南極は、ほかの大陸と同じように地形の変化に富んでいます。③エルスワース山脈、やまと山脈などの山脈があります。④最高峰であるヴィンソン・マシフ山は標高4,892メートルと、アルプスのマッターホルンをしのぎます。⑤北極は、氷に覆われた海です。⑥氷の厚さは平均10メートルぐらいで、南極のように標高が高い場所がありません。⑦一般的には、同緯度の場所を比較すると、海よりも陸、低地よりも高地の気温が低くなる傾向があります。⑧南極が寒いのも、陸地であり標高が高いという理由からです。⑨平均気温を比較すると、南極のほうが北極より20度ほど低いとされています。⑩また、地球上で観測された最低気温は、2010年8月10日に南極の東南極高原で記録されたマイナス93.2度です。

Why doesn't lake water soak into the bottom?

①The bottom of a lake is usually covered with
〜の底　　　　　　　　　　　　　　　　〜で覆われている
pebbles, sand, and so on. ②However, a lake is
小石　　　　　そのほか
always full of water. ③So, why doesn't lake water soak into
　　　〜で満ちている　では　　　　　　　　　　　　　〜にしみ込む
the bottom of a lake?

④Since the bottom of a lake is covered with pebbles, sand,
〜なので
soil, and so on, water actually soaks into the bottom.
土　　　　　　　　　　　　　実際には
⑤However, there are always layers of rock or clay under the
　　　　　　　　　　　　　　岩や粘土の層
bottom and these layers do not take in much water.
　　　　　　　　　　　　　　〜を取り込む
⑥The water which soaks into the pebbles and sand piles up
　　　　　　　　　　　　　　　　　　　　　　　　〜にたまる
on these layers. ⑦After that, some of the water flows away
　　　　　　　　　　　　　　　　　　　　　　　　　流れ出る
as underground water.
地下水として
⑧It is true that some water soaks into the bottom of a lake
確かに〜だが、—だ
or evaporates from the surface of the lake, but it seems that
　〜から蒸発する　　〜の表面
lake water does not soak into the bottom of a lake because

the same amount of water is added by rivers, rain, melted
同じ量の水　　　　　　　〜によって加えられる　　融けた〜
snow, and so on. (see p.67)

問22　湖の水はどうして、底にしみ込まないの？

答　①湖の底は多くの場合、小石や砂などで覆われています。②にもかかわらず、湖はいつも水をたたえています。③なぜ、湖の水は湖底にしみ込まないのでしょうか？

④湖の底は、小石や砂、土などで覆われており、水がしみ込みます。⑤しかし、その下には必ず岩や粘土の層があり、ほとんど水を通しません。⑥湖の底の砂や小石にしみ込んだ水は、この層の上にたまります。⑦そして、その一部は地下水となって流出します。

⑧湖底にしみ込んだり、湖面から蒸発する水もありますが、流れ込む川や、雨、雪どけによって水が補給されるために、湖の底に水がしみ込んでいないように見えるのです。

Q23

Why are snow crystals hexagonal?

①There are various shapes of snow crystals but
　　　　　さまざまな形の～　　　　　雪の結晶
perfectly formed ones are all hexagonal. ②If you
完璧に形づくられた　　　　　　　六角形の
look closely, you will find that not only snow
調べる　　　　　　　　　　　　～だけでなく―もまた
crystals but also ice crystals such as needle ice are
　　　　　　　　氷の結晶　　　　～のような　霜柱
hexagonal.

③A water molecule is made up of two hydrogen
　水の分子　　　　　　～で構成されている　　　　水素原子
atoms and one oxygen atom. ④Two hydrogen atoms form
　　　　　　酸素原子　　　　　　　　　　　　　　～を作る
an angle of 105 degrees. ⑤Because water molecules,
～の角度　　105度
composed of two atoms of hydrogen and one atom of
～で構成されている
oxygen, form three-dimensional and hexagonal ice crystals
　　　　　　3次元の(→立体的な)
with angles of 105 degrees. ⑥Although each angles of the
　　　　　　　　　　　　　　　　～だけれども
crystals are actually 105 degrees, regular hexagons with the
　　　　　　　　　　　　　　　　　正六角形
angles of 120 degrees can be seen from a certain angle.
　　　　　　　　　　　　　　　　　　　　　ある角度
⑦This is the most stabilized state for mass of the
　　　　　　最も安定した状態　　　　　　集まり
water molecules.

⑧The snow is ice crystals: the water vapor three-dimen-
　　　　　　　　　　　　　　　　　水蒸気

64

sionally crystallized in the chilled air. ⑨The snow crystals
　　　　　　結晶化した　　　　　　　冷えた
are formed based on the regular hexagon. ⑩Though the
　　　　　　　　　　　　　　　　　　　　　　　　　　　　　　　〜だが
crystals of the snow have a great variety in the
　　　　　　　　　　　　　　　　　　　いろいろな種類
shapes, hexagons can be seen from a certain angle.

(see p.67)

問23　　雪の結晶はなぜ、六角形なの？

答　①雪の結晶にはさまざまな形のものがありますが、美しく成長したものはすべて六角形です。②雪だけでなく、霜柱など氷の結晶を調べてみると、やはり六角形をしていることがわかります。

③水の分子は2個の水素原子と1個の酸素原子が結びついています。④2個の水素は、105度の角度を保っています。⑤1個の酸素原子と2個の水素原子でできた水の分子は、105度の角度のまま立体的な六方晶形の氷の結晶をつくるからです。⑥結晶のそれぞれの角は105度ですが、ある角度から見ると角が120度の正六角形に見えます。⑦これが水分子が集まって安定した状態です。

⑧雪は、水蒸気が冷たい空気中で立体的に結晶化したものです。⑨雪の結晶ができるときに基本となるのは、正六角形です。⑩雪の結晶にはいろいろな形がありますが、ある方向から見ると六角形に見えるのです。

地震の多くは、地球のプレートが
ぶつかり合って起きる

Most earthquakes happen when plates in the earth run into one another.

海洋プレート
Oceanic plates

大陸プレート
Continental plates

マントル
Mantle

大陸プレートや海洋プレートは、対流するマントルの上に浮いている

Continental plates and oceanic plates are floating on the convective mantle.

移動 / Moving

地震
Earthquake

大陸プレートに海洋プレートが潜り込むところに大きな力が蓄積されると、地震が起きる

An earthquake happens because of a heavily loaded part in which an oceanic plate get under a continental plate may give way.

湖の水がなくならないのは、湖底に水を通さない層があるから

A lake is always full of water because there are layers under the bottom and these layers do not take in water.

雨などで水分が補給される
Some water is added by rain and so on.

湖面から水分が蒸発する
Some water evaporates from the surface of the lake.

地下水として流出する
Some water flows away as underground water.

岩や粘度の層で保水する
Water is retained on the layers of rock or clay.

湖
Lake

岩や粘度の層
The layers of rock or clay

雪の結晶の形は、ある角度から六角形に見える

Snow crystals are seen regular hexagons from a certain angle

雪の結晶は複雑な形をしているが、ある角度から見ると正六角形に見える

Although a snow crystal has a complicated shape, you can find a regular hexagon when you see it from a certain angle.

Q24 Why does it snow though the temperature is not below 0 degrees C?

①Snow is ice crystals formed from water vapor: 〜から形成された 水蒸気

high up in the sky, frozen water vapor forms ice
上空で

particles and they grow to form larger crystals as they fall.
氷の粒　　　　　　　　　　　　　　　　　　　　　　　　　　　〜する間に

②It snows when it is below 0 degrees C up in the air
　　　　　　　　　　　　　氷点下　　　　　　　　上空で

regardless of the temperature on the ground. ③You may
〜に関係なく　　地上の気温

think, "Why does not snow melt into rain as it falls
　　　　　　　　　　　　　融けて雨になる　　〜するとき

when the temperature on the ground is above 0 degrees C?"
　　　　　　　　　　　　　　　　　　　　　　　0℃より高い

④Even when it is warmer than 0 degrees C, it sometimes
〜のときでさえ

snows without the snow melting. ⑤This is because snow
　　　雪が融けることなく　　　　　これは〜だからだ

needs heat around it when it melts. ⑥Heat is needed to raise
　　　熱　　　　　　　　　　　　　　　　　　〜を上昇させるために

the temperature of snow to 0 degrees C, the melting point
　　　　　　　　　　　　　　　　　　　　　　　　　　　氷の融点

of ice. ⑦It needs more heat to melt snow. ⑧It needs as

much as about 334.72 kilojoule of heat per kilogram
〜もの　　　　　334.72キロジュールの熱　　　　1キログラムあたり

when ice melts and turns into water. ⑨This amount of heat
　　　　　　　　　　　　　　　　　　　　　　　この熱量

can raise the same amount of water from 0 degrees C to
　　　　　同量の水

80 degrees C.

68

⑩That is why snow stays on the ground without melting
そういうわけで　　　　　　地面に残る
even when you feel warm. ⑪For the same reason, snow
同じ理由から
sometimes falls on the ground without melting in the air
even when the temperature is above 0 degrees C.

問24　気温が零度以下でなくても、なぜ雪が降るの？

答 ①雪は、上空で水蒸気が冷やされてできた氷の粒が、落下中に成長して大きな結晶となったものです。②地上の気温に関係なく、上空が氷点下なら雪になります。③「地上の気温が0℃以上だったら、雪は空中で融けて雨になるのでは？」と思うでしょう。

④気温が0℃より高くても、雪が融けずに降ることがあります。⑤これは、雪が融けるとき、周囲の熱が必要だからです。⑥まず雪の温度を融点の0℃まで上昇させるために熱が必要です。⑦雪が融けるには、さらに熱が必要です。⑧氷が融けて水になるためには、1キログラムあたり約334.72キロジュールもの熱が必要なのです。⑨これは同量の水を0℃から80℃まで温めることができるほどの熱量です。⑩ポカポカと暖かく感じても、積もった雪が融けずに残るのは、このような理由からです。⑪気温が0℃以上でも、雪が空中で融けることなく地上に達することがあるのも、同じ理由です。

世界地図をみてみよう

Let's see the world map.

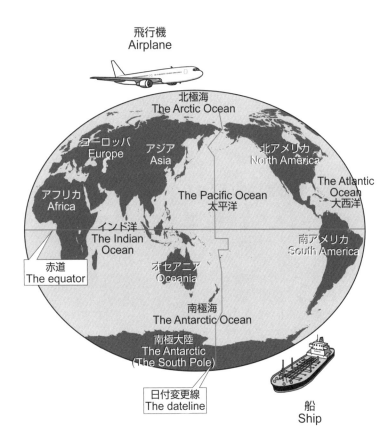

飛行機
Airplane

北極海
The Arctic Ocean

ヨーロッパ
Europe

アジア
Asia

北アメリカ
North America

The Atlantic
Ocean
大西洋

アフリカ
Africa

The Pacific Ocean
太平洋

インド洋
The Indian
Ocean

南アメリカ
South America

赤道
The equator

オセアニア
Oceania

南極海
The Antarctic Ocean

南極大陸
The Antarctic
(The South Pole)

日付変更線
The dateline

船
Ship

Questions about creatures

··

第３章

生き物の疑問

Q 25　Why did the dinosaurs die out?

①It is said that dinosaurs, which ruled the world
　　～といわれている　　　恐竜　　　　　　　～を支配した
for about 150 million years from over 200
　約1億5000万年間　　　　　　　　　　～以上
million years ago, died out 65 million years ago at the end
　　　　　　　　　　絶滅した
of the Mesozoic era in the Cretaceous period. ②There are
　　　中生代　　　　　　　　　　白亜紀
various hypotheses about why they died out: attributing it to
さまざまな仮説　　　　　　　　　　　絶滅した　　　～のせいにする
epidemic, a volcanic eruption, and so on. ③The most
伝染病　　　　火山の爆発　　　　　　　　　　　　最も有力な
influential among them is a meteor strike.
影響力のある　　　　　　　　　　隕石 (メテオ)衝突説
④The basis for this hypothesis is a thin layer of metal, iridium,
　　　根拠　　　　　　　　　　　　　金属の薄い層　　　　イリジウム
which covers the layer of the time when dinosaurs are thought
　　　　　　　　　　　　　　　　　　～である時代　　　　絶滅したと思われる
to have died out. ⑤The iridium layer is found all over the
world. ⑥Since there is almost no iridium on earth, it is thought
that this metal was brought to earth by a meteor or something
　　　　　　　　　～にもたらされた
like that. ⑦Scientists say that a huge meteor, which struck the
　　　　　　　　　　　　　　　　　巨大な　　　　　～に衝突した
earth at the end of the Cretaceous period and made a crater of
　　　　　　　　　　　　　　　　　　　　　　　　　　クレーター
about 180 kilometers across on the Yucatan Peninsula, formed
　　　　　　　　　直径　　　　　ユカタン半島　　　　～をつくった
this layer.

⑧This huge meteor is about 10 kilometers across and, when it

72

struck the earth, it might have given off energy about 5 billion
　　　　　　　　　　　　　　～を放出したかもしれない

times as much as the atomic bomb dropped over Hiroshima.
～の一倍の　　　　　　　　原子爆弾　　　　～に投下された

⑨The most believable theory says that, because of this strike,
　　　　　　信ずべき

little sunlight reached the surface of the earth on account of
ほとんどない　　　　　　　　表面　　　　　　　　　～のために

the great deal of dust with iridium which rose up, causing the
大量の粉塵　　　　　　　　　　　　　　舞い上がった

whole earth to get colder and dinosaurs to die out.

問25　恐竜はなぜ、絶滅したの？

答　①2億年以上前から約1億5000万年間、地球を支配したとされる恐竜が絶滅したのは、今から約6500万年前にあたる中生代白亜紀の末期だといわれています。②その理由については、伝染病説、火山の爆発などさまざまな説があります。③そのなかでも有力視されているのが、隕石衝突説です。

④その根拠となるのは、恐竜が絶滅したと思われる時代の地層を覆う、イリジウムという金属の薄い層です。⑤これは世界各地で発見されています。⑥イリジウムは、地球にはほとんど存在しないため、隕石などによって宇宙からもたらされたと考えられます。⑦イリジウムの層をつくったのは、白亜紀末期に地球に衝突し、ユカタン半島に直径約180キロメートルのクレーターをつくった巨大隕石だと考えられています。

⑧この巨大隕石は直径約10キロメートルほどもあり、衝突時のエネルギーは、広島型原爆の約50億倍と推定されています。⑨衝突により、イリジウムを含む大量の粉塵が舞い上がって地表に届く太陽光線が減少した結果、地球全体が寒冷化し、恐竜が絶滅したという説が有力です。

Q 26 Why do animals have two sexes, male and female?

①Some species have one sex but can reproduce
　　　　　　種　　　　　　性　　　　　　　　繁殖する
themselves. ②One example of this is potatoes in
　　　　　　　　　　例　　　　　　　　　　　ジャガイモ
the ground. ③Although potato plants produce flowers and
地中の　　　　　　　　　　植物としてのジャガイモ　花が咲き実を結ぶ
fruits, the potato, a part of the underground stem, is
　　　　　　　　　　　　　　　　　　　地下茎
produced without pollination. ④If you put a potato in the
　　　　　　　受精なしに　　　　　　　　埋めると, 〜
ground, it will put out buds and its "child" grows up. ⑤A
　　　　　　　　芽を出す
"child" reproduced without pollination in this way is a
　　　　繁殖された〜
clone which has the same genes as its "parent". ⑥This
クローン　　　　　　　　　〜と同じ遺伝子　　　親
means, if the "parent" is sensitive to the cold, the "child"
つまり　　　　　　　　〜に弱い
is also sensitive to the cold.

⑦Mammals such as human beings reproduce themselves
哺乳類　　　　　　　人間
with fertilization, in which the female's egg nucleus and
(動物が)生殖して　　　　　　　　雌の卵の核
the male's sperm nucleus unite, and the child gets two
雄の精子の核　　　　　　　合体する
halves of the genes which each of the parents has. ⑧In this
〜の半分ずつ　　　　　両親のそれぞれが持つ〜
case, even if the child's father is sensitive to the cold, the
　　　　〜だとしても
child is not always sensitive to the cold. ⑨Mammals can
　　　　　〜だとは限らない

74

have various children because of the combination of the
さまざまな　　　　　　　　　　　　　組み合わせ
male's and the female's genes. ⑩A child of parents who are

likely to be infected by a certain virus is sometimes not
〜しやすい　〜に感染する　　特定のウィルス
likely to be infected by the virus.

問26　動物はなぜ、雄と雌に分かれているの？

答 ①生物の中には、雄と雌がいなくても子孫を増やせる種もあります。②たとえば、土の中にできるジャガイモです。③ジャガイモには花が咲き実もできますが、ジャガイモのいもは地下茎の一部であり、受精とはまったく関係なくできます。④これを土に埋めておけば、芽が出て「子」が育ちます。⑤このように、受精なしにできた子は、親とまったく同じ遺伝子を持つクローンです。⑥つまり、親が寒さに弱い個体だとすると、子も寒さに弱くなります。

⑦人間をはじめとする哺乳類のように、雌の卵の核と雄の精子の核とが合体する受精によって子ができる場合には、子は両親の遺伝子を半分ずつ受け継ぎます。⑧この場合、父親が寒さに弱いとしても、母親の遺伝子も受け継いでいる子は寒さに弱くなるとは限りません。⑨雄と雌の遺伝子の組み合わせにより多様な子孫を残せるのです。⑩同様に、特定のウィルスに感染しやすい個体の子孫が、同じウィルスに感染しにくくなることもあります。

Q 27 Why Can Sparrows perch on Electric Wires?

①You can sometimes see sparrows or crows
<u>スズメ</u> <u>カラス</u>
perched on the stripped overhead wires of the
<u>〜にとまる</u> <u>むき出しの</u> <u>電車の架線</u>
railroad. ②Why don't they get an electric shock?
<u>感電する</u>

③Electric shock occurs when an electric current flows
<u>感電</u> <u>起こる</u> <u>電流</u> <u>〜を流れる</u>
through the body. ④An electric current flows through the
<u>through</u>
body when each of the two points on the body touches
<u>〜のそれぞれ</u> <u>体の2点</u>
two things which have different voltages. ⑤Birds perch
<u>異なった電圧</u>
on one electric wire with both legs. ⑥Even if 1,000 volts
<u>電線</u> <u>両足で</u> <u>〜としても</u>
are applied to this electric wire, they do not get
<u>1000ボルトの電圧がかかる</u>
an electric shock because both of their legs are touching
<u>〜の両方</u>
the electric wire.

⑦You are in danger of getting an electric shock when you
<u>〜する危険がある</u>
fly a kite and it gets caught on the overhead wires of the
<u>凧をあげる</u> <u>〜にひっかかる</u>
railroad. ⑧That's because the ground has 0 volts and the
<u>それは〜だからだ</u> <u>地面</u>
overhead wires of the railroad have 1,000 volts or

something. ⑨An electric current flows through the kite line
<u>凧糸を通って</u>

to you, and then, to the ground because these two points have different voltages. (see p.80)

問27　スズメはなぜ、電線にとまっても平気なの？

答 ①スズメやカラスは平気で電線がむき出しになった電車の架線などにとまっていることがあります。②なぜ、感電しないのでしょうか。

③感電とは、体に電流が流れて衝撃を受けることをいいます。④体に電流が流れるのは、電圧に差がある二つのものを体の2点で触れたときです。⑤鳥は一本の電線に両足をそろえてとまります。⑥その電線がたとえ1000ボルトだとしても、両足ともに1000ボルトに触れていることになり、感電しません。

⑦凧あげをしているとき、凧が電車の架線にひっかかった場合などは、感電する危険があります。⑧架線の電圧が1000ボルトだとして、地面は常に0ボルトです。⑨2点に電圧の差があるため、凧糸―人間―地面と電流が流れるからです。

Q 28 Why do migratory birds fly in a V-formation?

①Migratory birds move their wings up and down
渡り鳥　　　　　　　　　翼　　　上下に
when they fly. ②When they lower their wings, the
　　　　　　　　　　　～を下げる
air pressure under the wings becomes higher than that of
気圧　　　　　　　　　　　　　　　翼の上の気圧
above them and this provides lifting power. ③This lifting
～を与える　揚力
power make birds fly in the sky.

④When birds move their wings, the flow of air changes
空気の流れ
around the tip of the wings. ⑤This is because some of the
～の先　　　　　　　　　これは～だからだ
air pushed down by the wings goes up around the wings at
～によって押し下げられた—　　～の上に回り込む
both tips of the wings. ⑥This flow of air makes two
vortexes behind each wing of the flying bird. ⑦These are
渦
called wing-tip vortexes in aeronautics.
翼端渦　　　　　　　　航空学
⑧Air goes up in some parts of this flow of air and goes
～のある部分では
down in other parts of this flow of air making vortexes. ⑨A
～の別の部分では　　　　　渦を作りながら
bird flying behind the bird making vortexes finds it easy to
～のうしろを飛ぶ—
fly on the ascending air of the air flow.
上昇している空気に乗って飛ぶ
⑩Therefore migratory birds fly in a V-formation because
V字編隊で飛ぶ

the birds are following the ascending air of the wing-tip
<u>〜のあとを追っている</u>
vortexes made by the bird <u>flying ahead of them.</u> (see p.81)
<u>〜の前を飛んでいる—</u>

問28　渡り鳥はどうして、Vの字になって飛ぶの？

答 ①渡り鳥が飛んでいるときには、翼を上下に動かしています。②翼を下げたとき、翼の下の気圧が上の気圧よりも高くなり、揚力が発生します。③この揚力によって、鳥は空を飛ぶことができるのです。

④鳥が翼を動かすと、翼の先のほうだけは空気の流れが変わります。⑤翼の下に押し下げられた空気が、両翼の先端で上に回り込んでしまうからです。⑥この空気の流れは、飛んでいる鳥の後方で両翼分の2本の渦となります。⑦航空用語でいう翼端渦です。

⑧この空気の流れは渦を巻いていますから、空気が上昇しているところと下降するところがあります。⑨後続の鳥は、空気が上昇しているところを飛べば、楽に飛べるわけです。

⑩つまり、渡り鳥がV字編隊になるのは、すぐ前の鳥が残した翼端渦が上昇している部分を追って後続する鳥が飛んでいるからです。

両足の間に電圧差がなければ、鳥は感電しない

Birds do not get an electric shock if they touch, with both legs, two points which have same voltage.

| 1本の電線
One electric wire | 2本の電線
Two electric wires |

両足ともに 1000 ボルトであり、電圧に差がないため、電流が流れない

Its both legs touch the same voltage, 1000 volts, so no electric current flows through its body.

片足が 0 ボルト、もう一方の足が 1000 ボルトなら、両足に 1000 ボルトの電圧差があるため、大きい電流が流れる

One of its legs touches 0 volt and the other touches 1000 volts, in which voltage difference are 1000 volts, so a large electric current flows through its body.

渡り鳥は、前の鳥が作った 空気の渦の上を飛ぶのでV字になる

Migratory birds fly in a V-formation because a bird flies on the vortex made by the bird flying ahead of it.

気圧が低い
Air pressure is low.

翼端渦
Wing-tip vortex

気圧が高い
Air pressure is high.

翼の先で渦状の空気の流れができる
A vortex flow of air is made around
the tip of the wing.

V字
V-formation

うしろに続く鳥は、前の鳥が作った渦が上昇
するところにいると、楽に飛べる
A bird can fly easily by following the
ascending air of the vortexes made by the
bird flying ahead of it.

Q29　Fish don't close their eyes but don't they sleep?

①Some fish such as <u>gray shark</u> or <u>goggle-eyed</u>
　　　　　　　　　　　メジロザメ　　　　ムツゴロウ
gobies have a <u>membrane</u> in their eyes, which
　　　　　　　　 メムブレイン
　　　　　　　　　膜
takes the place of eyelids. ②<u>Sunfish</u> have <u>muscles</u> around
〜の代わりをする　　　 まぶた　　 マンボウ　　　　筋肉
the eye and they cover the eye, so they sometimes <u>look as if</u>

they are blinking. ③However, most of fish do not have
まばたきしているかのように見える
eyelids and they <u>keep their eyes open</u>. ④You may think that
　　　　　　　　 眼を開け続ける
fish do not sleep because they keep their eyes open, but

every fish <u>does sleep</u>.
　　　　　 実際には眠る
⑤The time and place of sleeping <u>depend on</u> the <u>kind of</u> fish.
　　　　　　　　　　　　　　　 〜による　　　 〜の種類
⑥<u>Flounders</u>, <u>right-eyed flounders</u>, and <u>congers</u>, which are
　 ヒラメ　　　 カレイ　　　　　　　　 アナゴ
<u>active</u> at night, sleep during the day, and <u>parrot bass</u>,
活発な　　　　　　　　　　　　　　　　　　　　　 イシダイ
filefish, and <u>rockfish</u> sleep at the night.
カワハギ　　　 メバル
⑦The place of sleeping depends on the kind of fish, but

they all sleep in a place which is <u>safe from attack</u> such as
　　　　　　　　　　　　　　　　　 攻撃に対して安全な
space <u>between rocks or in the sand</u>.
　　　 岩の間や砂の中といった〜
⑧<u>Migratory fish</u> like <u>tuna</u> are always swimming, so they
　 回遊魚　　　　　 マグロ

82

sleep while swimming. ⑨However, if they fell fast asleep,
　　　　　　　　　　　　　　　　　熟睡するなら
they would not be able to swim. ⑩They are swimming
　　泳ぐことができないだろう
while sleeping lightly.
　　　　　　浅く

問29　　魚は眼を閉じないけれど、寝ないの？

答　①メジロザメ、ムツゴロウなど一部の魚は、まぶたの役割をする膜を持ちます。②マンボウは眼の周囲の筋肉が眼を覆い、まばたきしているように見えることがあります。③しかし、ほとんどの魚にはまぶたがなく、いつも眼を開けています。④眠っているときも眼を開けているため、眠らないように見えますが、どんな魚も必ず眠ります。

⑤眠る時間や場所は、種類によって異なります。⑥夜行性のヒラメ、カレイ、アナゴなどは昼間に眠り、イシダイ、カワハギ、メバルなどは夜眠ります。

⑦眠る場所も魚の種類によって違い、岩の間や砂の中など敵に攻撃されにくい場所です。

⑧マグロのように、常に泳ぎ続けている回遊魚は、泳ぎながら眠ります。⑨といっても、完全に眠ってしまうと泳ぎ続けることなどできないはずです。⑩半分眠ったうとうと状態で眠りながら泳いでいるのです。

Q30 Why can salmon live both in the sea and the rivers?

①The important difference between fresh water and
~と―の間の違い　　　淡水

salt water for fish is osmotic pressure. ②Water flows
塩水　　　　　　浸透圧　　　　　　流れる

from water with low osmotic pressure to that with high
浸透圧が低い水　　　　　　　　浸透圧が高い水

osmotic pressure. ③The osmotic pressure of seawater is higher
海水

than that of fresh water. ④The osmotic pressure of the body fluid of
体液

fresh water fish and seawater fish is almost the same; the pressure is
淡水魚　　　　　海水魚

just between that of seawater and fresh water. ⑤Therefore, even
~の中間

when fresh water fish are in fresh water, they are in danger
~する危険がある

of swelling up because their body takes in water. ⑥In contrast,
ふくれ上がること　　　　　　~を取り入れる　　　逆に

even when seawater fish are in salt water, they are in danger

of shedding too much water. ⑦It is the osmotic pressure
~を流し出すこと　　　　　　浸透圧調整機能

adjustment function that controls this. ⑧Fresh water fish reduce
~を調整する　　　　　　　　　　　~を減らす

the amount of water in their bodies by urinating a lot. ⑨On the
ユアリネイティング
尿をすること　　　一方

contrary, seawater fish try not to urinate a lot and, at the
~しないようにする

same time, they give off salt through their gills.
~を出す　　　　エラ

⑩Fish which move from the sea to the rivers and from the

rivers to the sea such as salmon and eel are called

サケ　　　　　ウナギ

euryhaline fish. ⑪Euryhaline fish have an osmotic pressure

ユーレヘイライン

広塩性魚

adjustment function which allows them to live both in the

〜に—させる

sea and in rivers and can use it well in both types of water.

⑫Therefore they can live both in the sea and in rivers.

(see p.90)

問30　サケはどうして、海と川の両方で生きていけるの？

答　①魚にとって、淡水と塩水の大きな違いは浸透圧です。②水分は浸透圧が低いほうから高いほうへと移動します。③海水と淡水を比べると、浸透圧が高いのは海水です。④淡水魚と海水魚の体液の浸透圧はほぼ同じで、海水と淡水の中間の浸透圧です。⑤これが原因で、淡水魚は淡水中にいるとき、体が水を吸収し水ぶくれ状態になる危険にさらされています。⑥逆に、海水魚は塩水中にいると、水分が流出してしまう危険があります。⑦これを調整するのが、浸透圧調整機能です。⑧淡水魚は尿として多くの水分を排出し、体内の水分を減らします。⑨海水魚は逆に水分をあまり出さないようにすると同時に、エラから塩分を排出しています。

⑩サケやウナギのように川から海へ、海から川へと回遊する魚は、広塩性魚と呼ばれています。⑪広塩性魚は海水にも淡水にも対応する浸透圧調整機能を持ち、淡水と海水でこれを使い分けることができます。⑫そのため、川でも海でも生きていけるのです。

Q 31 Don't lions become sick though they eat only meat, not vegetables?

①It is said that people who eat only meat are
肉
likely to suffer from lifestyle diseases. ②Now,
〜しやすい 〜(病気など)にかかる 生活習慣病
you may wonder if meat-eating animals such as lions are
〜だろうかと思う 肉食動物
healthy.
健康な

③It is known that animals in the cat family such as lions
猫科
especially eat only meat. ④The members of the cat family
特に
have a body system which keeps them healthy through
体のしくみ 健康を保つ〜 〜によって
eating only meat. ⑤One of the reasons lies in
〜にある
L-gulonolactone oxidase. ⑥Since the meat-eating animals
L-グロノラクトン 酸化酵素
such as the members of the cat family have this oxidase,

they can make Vitamin C from grape sugar in their bodies.
ニュートリエンツ ビタミンC ブドウ糖
⑦The nutrients they can't make in their bodies such as
栄養素
Vitamin A are taken in by eating grass-eating animals.
ビタミンA 取り入れられる 草食動物
⑧The meat-eating animals take in vitamins through eating

grass-eating animal's livers.
肝臓
⑨Properly digested plants staying in the stomach and the
適度に消化された 胃腸

intestine of the grass-eating animals are also important

source of vitamins for them.
ビタミン源

問31　ライオンは肉ばかり食べて野菜を食べなくても、病気にならないの？

答　①人間は、肉ばかり食べていると生活習慣病にかかりやすくなるといわれています。②そこで気になるのが、ライオンなどのように肉ばかり食べている肉食獣の健康です。③ライオンなどの猫科の動物は、特に強い肉食性を持っていることが知られています。④猫科の動物は、肉ばかり食べていても健康を保てるような体のしくみを持っているのです。⑤その一例がL-グロノラクトン酸化酵素です。⑥猫科をはじめとする肉食獣はこの酵素を持っているため、体内でブドウ糖からビタミンCを合成することができます。⑦ビタミンAなどの体内で合成できないものは、草食動物を食べることによって補います。⑧肉食動物は草食動物の肝臓を食べることによって、ビタミンを摂取します。

⑨草食動物や肉食動物の胃や小腸にある、適度に消化された植物も重要なビタミン源です。

Q32 Why do sunflowers always face to the sun?

①It is only growing sunflowers that follows the
〜するのは—だ　成長している　ヒマワリ
direction of the sun. ②Sunflowers which are in
〜の方向
their growth period and have not started to bloom yet, face
成長期　　　　　　　　　　　　　　　　　　　　　　　空をむく
the sky at night, face east in the morning, and turn their
　　　　　　　　東をむく
faces from east to west to follow the sun in the daytime.
　　　　　　　　　　　　　太陽の動きを追って
③This is the movement of the plants by a nature named
　　　　　　　　　　　　　　　　　　　　　　　　性質
phototropism.
屈光性
④Phototropism of plants such as that of sunflowers is the

nature caused by a kind of growth hormones named auxin.
　　　　〜によって起こる—　　　成長ホルモン　　　　　オーキシン
⑤When this hormone reaches an amount, the plant speeds
　　　　　　　　　　　一定量に達する　　　　　　　　〜を早める
up its growth.
　　成長
⑥The reason why the plants face to the sun is that the auxin

moves to the side of their stem which does not catch
　　　　　　茎の側　　　　　　　　　　　　　　太陽光線を受ける
sunlight. ⑦As a result, the amount of auxin is small on the
　　　　　　その結果　　〜の量
side of the stem which catches sunlight and the amount of it

on the side of the stem which does not catch sunlight is

good enough to grow up. ⑧The head of sunflower faces to
<u>～するのに十分な</u>

the sun because only the side of the stem which does not

catch sunlight speeds up its growth <u>thanks to</u> <u>the difference</u>
　　　　　　　　　　　　　　　　　　～のために　　　～の違い

in the amount of auxin between those sides.
<u>　</u>

問32　ヒマワリの花はどうして、太陽のほうをむいているの？

答　①花が太陽の方向を追うように動くのは、成長期のヒマワリだけです。②花が咲く前の成長期のヒマワリは、夜は上をむき、朝になると東をむき、日中は太陽の移動に合わせて南から西の方向に頭を回転させます。③これは、植物の屈光性（くっこうせい）と呼ばれる動きの一つです。

④ヒマワリをはじめとする植物の屈光性は、オーキシンと呼ばれる成長ホルモンの一種によるものです。⑤これが適度な濃度になると、植物は成長を早めます。

⑥植物が太陽の方向をむくのは、オーキシンが茎の中で光が当たらない方向に移動するからです。⑦その結果、茎（くき）の光が当たっている側のオーキシン濃度は低く、光があたらない側で成長に適した濃度になります。⑧ヒマワリの花が太陽の方向をむくのは、オーキシンの濃度差により、光が当たらない側だけ成長が早まるからです。

サケは、海水中と淡水中で、体内の水分と塩分を調整する

Salmons can control water and salt in them both in fresh water and in salt water.

浸透圧
Osmotic pressure

水分は浸透圧が低いほうから高いほうへ移動する
Liquid flows from water with low osmotic pressure to that with high osmotic pressure.

高 / Higher

低 / Lower

海水 Seawater

淡水 Fresh water

サケの体液の浸透圧は、淡水と海水の中間
Osmotic pressure of the body fluid of salmon is just between that of seawater and fresh water.

海水中では、水分はサケの体内から出ようとする
In seawater, water in salmon's body is likely to come out.

淡水中では、水分はサケの体内に入り込もうとする
In fresh water, water is likely to go into salmon's body.

薄い尿をたくさん排出
They pass a watery urine a lot.

エラから塩分を吸収
They take in salt through their gills.

エラから塩分を排出
They give off salt through their gills.

濃い尿を少し排出
They pass a salty urine a little.

ひまわりの茎は、日陰側が活発に成長する

The side of the sunflowers' stem which does not catch sunlight grows well.

植物の成長ホルモンであるオーキシンは、太陽光が当たらない部分に移動する。

Auxin, a kind of plant growth hormone, moves to the part which does not catch sunlight.

日陰
Shade

日なた
Sunshine

オーキシンが多い日陰側は細胞分裂が活発なので、成長が早い。

The side of the sunflowers' stem which does not catch sunlight and has much auxin grows fast because it undergoes cell division actively.

Q33 Why don't penguins live in the North Pole?

①You will probably be surprised to hear that

　　　　　　　　　　　　　　　　　　～して驚く

penguins used to live at the North Pole. ②In fact,

ペンギン　もとは～した　　北極

オークス

great auks living in the North Pole were commonly called

オオウミガラス　　　　　　　　　　　　　　　　　～と俗称された

"penguin" in the old days. ③Unfortunately, people hunted

　　　　　　　　　　　　　残念ながら　　　　　　　～を狩った

them too much and they died out in the 1840's.

　　　　　　　　　　　　　絶滅した　　1840年代に

④Around that time, Europeans often went to look around

　　　　　　　　　　　ヨーロッパ人　　　　　　　探検する

the southern hemisphere and they found a new kind of bird

南半球

living around cold seaside in the southern hemisphere.

寒い海辺に住んでいる～

⑤Since the birds looked like the great auks, they came to

　　　　　　　　　　～に似ている　　　　　　　　　　　　～と呼ばれるようになった

be called penguin. ⑥They are the penguins we know today.

⑦Academically, these two kinds of birds are not closely

　学術的には　　　　　　　　　　　　　　　　　　　近い関係ではない

related because great auks are Charadriiformes and

近い関係ではない　　　　　　　　　　　　　　チドリ目の

　　　　　　　　スフェニシフォームズ

penguins are Sphenisciformes. ⑧However, great auks were

　　　　　　　ペンギン目の

like penguins today.

⑨Both great auks and penguins could not cross the equator

　　　　　　　　　　　　　　　　　　　　　　　～を横切る　赤道

because they did not like heat. ⑩Scientists think that these

　　　　　　　　　　　暑さ

academically different birds became similar in the course
学術的に異なった　　　　　　　　　似た　　　進化の過程において
of evolution in a similar environment.
似た環境のもとで

問33　ペンギンはどうして、北極にはいないの？

答 ①「ペンギンは、もともと北極にいた鳥」だと聞くと、みなさんは驚くに違いありません。②実は「ペンギン」はもともと、北極にいたオオウミガラスにつけられた俗称でした。③残念なことに、この鳥は人間に乱獲され、1840年代に絶滅してしまいました。④ちょうどその頃、ヨーロッパ人による南半球の探検が盛んになり、南半球の寒い海辺に生息する新種の鳥が発見されました。⑤この鳥はオオウミガラスに似ていたためペンギンと呼ばれるようになりました。⑥これが現在のペンギンです。

⑦オオウミガラスはチドリ目であるのに対して、ペンギンはペンギン目であり、この2種類の鳥は分類上は近い仲間とはいえません。⑧にもかかわらず、オオウミガラスは現在のペンギンと同じような姿をした鳥でした。

⑨ペンギンもオオウミガラスも、暑さが苦手であるため赤道を横切って移動できなかったのでしょう。⑩その一方で、分類上まったく異なる鳥が似た環境のもとで進化するうちに、似た姿になったものと考えられています。

Q34　Why do ants walk in line?

①You sometimes see ants walking in line in
〔〜が―するのを見る〕　〔アリ〕　〔列になって〕
parks or in your garden. ②The ants' line is

sometimes more than 50 meters long. ③An ant follows the
　　　　　　　〔50メートル以上の長さ〕　　　　〔〜のあとをついて行く〕
ant ahead of it even when they walk a long way.
〔自分の前のアリ〕　〔〜するときでさえ〕
④Ants walk in line mainly when they go out for food.
　　　　　　　　　　〔主に〜するときに〕　　　　　〔〜を求めて〕〔餌〕
⑤When an ant finds food, it releases chemical substance
　　　　　　　　　　　　　　　〔〜を出す〕　〔化学物質〕
from its body to make a trail and goes back to the nest
　　　　　　　　　　　〔足跡(→目印)〕
with the food. ⑥This chemical substance, with which ants

make a trail, is called pheromone. ⑦When the ant which
　　　　　　　　　　　〔フェロモン〕
has found food comes back to its nest, other ants in the nest

start to go to the place where the food is following the trail
　　　　　　　　　　　　　　　　　　　　〔〜をたどりながら〕
pheromone. ⑧This forms the ants' line.
　　　　　　　　〔〜を形づくる〕
⑨Ants can do almost nothing with the help of their vision
　　　　　　〔〜することがほとんどない〕〔〜を頼りにして〕　　　〔視覚〕
because their vision is very poor. ⑩Instead, they use their
　　　　　　　　　　　　　〔劣っている〕　〔その代わりに〕
antennae to touch something and find out what it is, and
〔触角〕　　　　　　　　　　　　　〔それが何であるかを見つけ出す〕
also use pheromone as a means of sending messages.
　　　　　　　　　　〔〜の手段として〕〔伝言を送ること (→情報伝達)〕

(see p.100)

94

問34　アリはどうして、行列をつくって歩くの？

答 ①公園や庭で、アリが行列をつくって歩いているところを見かけることがあります。②長さは時には50メートルを超えることもあります。③そんなに長い距離でも、後ろを歩くアリは前を歩くアリが歩いたあとをたどります。

④アリが行列をつくるのは、主に餌（えさ）を探しに行くときです。⑤1匹のアリが餌を見つけると、腹部から目印になる物質を出しながら餌を抱（かか）えて巣に戻ります。⑥目印となるのは、フェロモンと呼ばれる物質です。⑦餌を見つけたアリが巣にたどり着くと、巣にいたアリたちは帰ってきたアリのフェロモンをたどり、餌の場所を目指します。⑧これがアリの行列です。

⑨アリは目がそれほど発達していないので、視覚に頼ることはほとんどできません。⑩それを補うのが、ものに触れて確認するための触角と、情報伝達の手段としてのフェロモンなのです。

①Fish living at a depth over 200 meters
<u>水深200メートル以下に住んでいる～</u>
are generally called deep-sea fish. ②Water pressure
<u>深海魚</u>　　　　　　　　　<u>水圧</u>
at a depth of 200 meters is about 20 bar. ③An empty PET
<u>20気圧</u>　　<u>空の</u>　<u>ペットボトル</u>
bottle (Polyethylene terephthalate bottle) with a cap sunk
<u>ポリエチレンテレフタラートボトル</u>　<u>キャップをした</u>　<u>～に沈められた</u>
to this depth will be crushed flat under this pressure.
　　　　　　　　<u>～でペシャンコになる</u>

④Then, why aren't deep-sea fish crushed under such pressure?
<u>それでは</u>

⑤Fish living in shallow water such as <u>horse mackerel</u> and
　　　　　　　　　　　　　　　　<u>アジ</u>
sardine have <u>air bladders</u> which enable them to rise and
<u>イワシ</u>　　<u>うきぶくろ</u>
fall in the water <u>according to</u> <u>the amount of</u> air in them.
　　　　　　<u>～によって</u>　<u>～の量</u>

⑥The <u>specific gravity</u> of sea fish is higher than that of <u>the</u>
　　　　<u>比重</u>
<u>seawater</u>, so they can not <u>come up</u> <u>without</u> the air bladders.
<u>海水</u>　　　　　　　　<u>浮上する</u>　<u>～なしで</u>

⑦Then, <u>what would happen</u> if horse mackerel or sardine
　　　　<u>何が起こるだろうか</u>
<u>went down to</u> the deep sea? ⑧They <u>would die</u> because their
<u>もし～へ潜って行ったら</u>　　　　　<u>死ぬだろう</u>
air bladders would be crushed. ⑨One of the reasons that

deep-sea fish can live <u>under high pressure</u> <u>lies in</u> their air
　　　　　　　　　<u>高い水圧のもとで</u>　<u>～にある</u>
bladder. ⑩The air bladder of deep-sea fish <u>is filled with</u> <u>fat</u>,
　　　　　　　　　　　　　　　　　　　<u>～で満たされている</u>　<u>脂肪</u>

and, in other points, they are also designed to live under
　　　　　　そのほかの点において　　　　　　　　　〜するように作られている

high pressure. ⑪Some deep-sea fish do not have an air

bladder. ⑫However, the secret of deep-sea fish is not well
　　　　　　　　　　　　　　　　　　　　　　　　　まだ〜ない

understood yet. ⑬Their mysteries will be solved in the near
よく理解されていない　　　　　　神秘　　　　　　解明される　　　近い将来

future.

問35　深海魚はなぜ、水圧に押しつぶされないの？

答 ①深海魚とは、一般的に水深200メートル以下の深海に生息する魚を指します。②水深200メートルの水圧は約20気圧。③空のペットボトルにふたをして沈めると、ペシャンコになってしまうほどの力を受けます。④深海魚はこれだけの圧力を受けているにもかかわらず、なぜつぶれないのでしょうか？⑤アジやイワシをはじめとした浅い海に暮らす魚は、空気の量で浮き沈みを調整するうきぶくろを持っています。⑥海水魚の比重は海水より重いため、うきぶくろがないと浮上することができません。⑦では、もしもアジやイワシが深海に行ったらどうなるでしょうか？⑧うきぶくろがつぶれて死んでしまうでしょう。⑨深海魚が強い水圧に耐えられる秘密の一つは、うきぶくろにあります。⑩深海魚のうきぶくろは、空気の代わりに脂肪で満たされるなど、高い水圧にも耐えられるような構造をしています。⑪なかには、うきぶくろを持たないものもいます。⑫ただし、深海魚についての研究はそれほど進んでいません。⑬今後、多くの謎が解き明かされることでしょう。

Q 36 Why do leaves turn red in autumn?

①As the temperature falls, plants become inactive and the amount of water taken in from the roots becomes less. ②The trees die from lack of water if all the water taken in from the roots evaporates from the leaves. ③Therefore trees shed their leaves to avoid water evaporation and get ready for the cold season.

④A separation layer is formed between the leaves and the branch when the temperature starts falling. ⑤The leaves look green because they have the chlorophyll which is necessary for photosynthesis. ⑥The chlorophyll is broken down because the separation layer blocks the water and the nutrients.

⑦In the case of the plants, such as maple, whose leaves turn red, the separation layer blocks the flows of the sugar which is produced in the leaves and send to the branches.

⑧As the result, a red coloring matter called anthocyanin is made up from the sugar and it makes leaves turn red.

⑨The leaves such as of <u>ginkgo</u> turn yellow because they
　　　　　　　　　　　　　イチョウ
have a yellow coloring matter called <u>carotinoid</u>.　⑩The
　　　　　　　　　　　　　　　　　　カロテノイド
color of carotenoid, which is always in leaves, comes to
<u>stand out</u> as the chlorophyll is broken down.
目立つ

問36　秋になると、なぜ葉っぱが赤くなるの？

答　①温度が下がると植物の活動が鈍り、根が吸い上げる水の量が減ります。②もしも根が吸い上げた水分がすべて葉から蒸発してしまうと、水分が不足して、木は枯れてしまいます。③そこで木は、水分の蒸発を防ぐために葉を落として、寒い季節に備えます。④気温が下がり始めると、葉と枝の間に離層が形成されます。⑤木の葉が緑色に見えるのは、植物が光合成を行なうのに必要な葉緑素があるからです。⑥しかしながら、離層ができると、それが水分や養分の流れを妨げるため、この葉緑素が分解されていきます。

⑦モミジのように赤く色づく植物の場合、葉でつくられた糖分が離層によって枝に送られなくなります。⑧その結果、この糖分からアントシアニンという赤い色素が合成されて、木の葉は赤くなります。⑨イチョウなどで葉が黄色くなるのは、カロテノイドという黄色の色素によるものです。⑩カロテノイドはもともと葉に含まれていますが、葉緑素が分解されることにより、カロテノイドの黄色が目立ってくるわけです。

アリはほかのアリが出したフェロモンを目印にする

Ants follow the trail pheromone other ants release.

餌をみつける
Finding food

餌を見つけたアリは、腹部からフェロモンを出しながら
巣に戻る
An ant which has found food comes back to its
nest releasing a pheromone from its body.

フェロモン
Pheromone

巣にいたアリがフェロモンをたどり、餌集めに出発する
Ants in the nest start to go to the place
in which there is food following the trail
pheromone.

多くのアリがフェロモンをたどって餌集めに行くため、
行列になる
A lot of ants go to get food following the
pheromone and form the line.

木の葉が紅葉するのは、赤い色素ができるから

The leaves turn red because a red coloring matter is made.

木の葉が紅葉するしくみ
How the leaves turn red

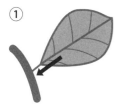

葉緑素によりでんぷんが作られ、幹に送られている

Starch is made by chlorophyll and sent to the trunk.

離層
Separation layer

寒くなると、葉緑素の働きが弱くなり、葉のつけ根に離層が形成される

Chlorophyll doesn't work well and a separation layer is formed at the root of a leaf when it becomes cold.

離層により幹に流れなくなった養分が葉にたまる。それが分解されて糖分になる

Nutrients stay in the leaves because the separation layer keeps them from entering the trunk. These nutrients are broken down into the sugar.

糖分から赤い色素であるアントシアニンが合成され、木の葉が赤く色づく

Anthocyanin, a red coloring matter, is made up from the sugar and the leaves turn red.

There are many different creatures on the earth.

ライオン
Lion

男女
Male and Female

象
Elephant

キリン
Giraffe

猫
Cat

トラ
Tiger

ニワトリ
Chicken

ねずみ
Mouse

アザラシ
Seal

パンダ
Panda

ひまわり
Sunflower

チューリップ
Tulip

Chapter 4

Questions
about
human body

第４章

人間の体の疑問

Q 37 Did human beings evolve from apes?

①Although all apes are grouped together, there
〜だが　　　サル　　一緒にされる
is a bigger difference between chimpanzees and
　　　　　　〜と—の間の違い　　　チンパンジー
Japanese monkeys than between chimpanzees and human
ニホンザル　　　　　　　　　　　　　　　　　　　　　ヒト
beings. ②It is chimpanzees that human beings are close to on
　　　　　〜なのは—だ　　　　　　　　　　　　　　〜に近い
the evolutionary tree. ③It is said that, about 5 million years ago,
進化の系統樹では　　　　　　　　　　　　　500万年前
chimpanzees and human beings separated from a kind of ape
　　　　　　　　　　　　　　　　　〜から分かれた
which has died out, and each of them evolved differently.
　　　　絶滅してしまった　　　　　　　　　進化した
④For a long time scientists could not find out what kind of
　長い間　　　　　　　　　　　　　　　〜を見つけ出す
ape the common ancestor of human beings and
　　　　共通の祖先
chimpanzees was. ⑤However, scientists today think that
one of the anthropoids whose fossils have been found such
　　　　　類人猿　　　　　　化石
as Nakalipithecus and Ouranopithecus, is the common
　　ナカリピテクス　　　　オウラノピテクス
ancestor of human beings and chimpanzees.

⑥In the study of genes, the difference between chimpanzees
　　　　　　　　　遺伝子
and human beings in DNA (deoxypentose nucleic acid)
　　　　　　　　　　　　　　　デオキシペントース核酸
sequence is within several percentage points. ⑦This
配列　　　　　　数パーセント以内

difference is very small in genetics. ⑧This small difference

in genes is a result of the different evolutions for as long as

遺伝学

結果　　　　　　　　　　　　進化　　　　　～もの

5 million years.

⑨Therefore it is wrong to say that human beings evolved

from apes. ⑩You should say that apes and human beings

have a common ancestor. (see p.116)

問37　ヒトはサルから進化したの？

答　①ひと言でサルといっても、チンパンジーとニホンザルでは、チンパンジーとヒト以上の違いがあります。②進化の系統から見てヒトと近いのは、チンパンジーです。③チンパンジーとヒトは、現在はいないサルと500万年ほど前に枝分かれし、ヒトとチンパンジーに分かれて進化したということです。④ヒトとチンパンジーの共通の祖先がどのようなサルであったのか、長い間わかりませんでした。⑤最近では、ナカリピテクス、オウラノピテクスなど、化石で発見された類人猿が、ヒトとチンパンジー共通の祖先と考えられています。

⑥遺伝子の研究では、チンパンジーとヒトとのDNA配列の違いは、数パーセント以内とされています。⑦この違いは、遺伝学的に見るとほんのわずかにすぎません。⑧このわずかな遺伝子の違いが500万年間にわたり、違う進化をしてきた結果なのです。

⑨したがって、「ヒトはサルから進化」したというのは正しくありません。⑩「サルとヒトの祖先は同じだ」というべきなのです。

Q 38 Why must all human beings die?

① Some scientists say that telomere has something
テロメア 〜と関係がある
to do with the life span of human beings.
〜の寿命

② Telomere is the tail-like part at the ends of chromosomes.
しっぽのような部分 〜の両端 クロウモソウムズ 染色体

③ Scientists say that telomere protects DNA, and that it is
〜を守る
also necessary for cells to divide in order to make new
〜が—するのに必要とされる 細胞 分裂する 〜するために
normal cells.
正常な

④ Most of the cells of living things divide to make new cells
生物の細胞
again and again. ⑤ Telomeres shorten every time cells
繰り返し 短くなる 〜が—するたびに
divide. ⑥ When telomeres become short after cells divide a
短くなる
certain number of times, the cells stop dividing. ⑦ It is
ある回数
thought that this is to prevent abnormal cell division such
避ける 異常な 分裂
as cancer, which is caused by telomeres which are not
癌
sufficiently active. ⑧ The state at which cells stop dividing is
〜である状態
called cell aging.
細胞の老化

⑨ Today, it is said that the life span of human beings is
about 120 years at longest. ⑩ It is believed that telomere
長くても
is one of the complicate factors which decide the life span
複雑な

of human beings.

問38　人間はなぜ、必ず死ぬの？

答　①人間の寿命にテロメアがかかわっている、という説があります。②テロメアというのは、染色体の両端にあるしっぽのような部分です。③このテロメアはDNAを守るだけでなく、正常に細胞分裂を行なうなどのために必要なものとされています。

④生物の多くの細胞は、分裂を繰り返しています。⑤テロメアは細胞分裂のたびに短くなっていきます。⑥そして、一定回数の細胞分裂を行ない、ある長さより短くなると、細胞は分裂をやめてしまいます。⑦これは、テロメアが十分に働かないことにより、癌化など、異常な細胞分裂を起こすことを防ぐためと考えられています。⑧細胞が分裂をやめたその状態が「細胞の老化」です。

⑨現在、人間の寿命は最長120歳前後とされています。⑩もちろん、人間の寿命を左右する要因は単純なものではありませんが、テロメアもその一つではないかと考えられています。

①There are some theories to explain why the
学説
human body is not covered with hair like
ヒトの身体　　　　　〜で覆われていない
most of the other mammals.
哺乳類

②One of them is the theory that human beings lost their hair
説　　　　　人類
to control their body temperature. ③When the ancestors
〜を調整する　　体温　　　　　　　　　　　　祖先
of human beings lived in trees, they were not exposed to direct
さらされた　　直射日光
sunlight. ④Later, when they began to walk upright and
のちに　　　　　〜するようになった　二足歩行する
live on grasslands, they had to work under the burning sun.
草原　　　　　　　　　　　　　炎天下で
⑤The theory is that, in order to adapt themselves to
〜に適応するために
these new surroundings, the sweat glands of human beings
環境　　　　　　汗腺
developed to control their body temperature by sweating and
発達して〜した　　　　　　　　　　　　　汗をかくことによって
that they lost their hair at the same time.
同時に

⑥Another one is called "Human Neoteny Theory."
人類ネオテニー説
⑦Neoteny means that animals grow old with the
〜の性質を持って
characteristics they have at birth. ⑧Newborn
出生時に持っている〜
chimpanzees have no hair. ⑨This theory is that human
生まれたばかりのチンパンジー

beings grow retaining the hairless feature of the juvenile
成長する　〜をとどめたままで　無毛の　特徴　幼年期
stage.

⑩There are other theories about this matter but none
　　　　　　　　　　　　　　　　　　この問題　　　　　〜のどれも一ない
of them have been confirmed yet.
　　　まだ確認されていない

**問39　ヒトはどうして、イヌやネコのように
全身が毛で覆われていないの？**

答　①ヒトがほかの哺乳類のように全身を体毛で覆われてい
ない理由については、いくつかの説があります。
②まず、体温を調整するために、体毛を失ったとする説です。
③ヒトの祖先が木の上で生活していたころには、直射日光にさ
らされることはありませんでした。④直立歩行を始め、草原で
暮らすようになると、炎天下で活動しなければならなくなりま
す。⑤この環境に合わせて、汗で体温調整ができるように汗腺
を発達させ、同時に体毛を失ったとするものです。
⑥もう一つは、「人類ネオテニー説」と呼ばれるものです。⑦ネ
オテニーとは生まれたばかりの性質を残したまま成熟すること
です。⑧生まれたばかりのチンパンジーには体毛がありません。
⑨ヒトは無毛という幼年期の特徴を備えたままで成長する生物
だとするものです。
⑩ほかにも諸説ありますが、まだ定説とされるものはありません。

Why do you shed tears when you are sad?

①The surface of the eye is always covered with thin layer of tears. ②This is because tears reduce the effect of stimuli from outside and protect the eye. ③You shed tears when you have something in your eye and it's surface is stimulated. ④This is because the trifacial nerve is working.

⑤Tears which come in the eye when you are sad or happy are different from tears which come in the eye when it is stimulated. ⑥This is because the autonomous nerve is working. ⑦The autonomous nerve is made up of the sympathetic nerve and the parasympathetic nerve. ⑧When you are very much excited by anger or regret, the sympathetic nerve works actively and a small amount of salty tears comes in the eye. ⑨When you are sad or moved, the parasympathetic nerve works actively and a large amount of watery tears comes in the eye.

⑩In tears, there are prolactin and adrenocorticotropic
　　　　　　　　　　　　プロラクチン　　　　　　副腎皮質刺激ホルモン
                                    アドリーノコーティコートロピク

hormones, which cause a state of tension under stress, and
　　　　　　　　　　　～を引き起こす　緊張状態　　　　ストレスにさらされて

manganese, a large amount of which is said to cause
マンガン　　　　　　　　　　　　　　　　　　　　～するといわれている

depression. ⑪Some scientists say that you feel good after you
うつ病

shed tears because these substances are passed out of the
　　　　　　　　　　　　　　　　　　　～から排出される

body with tears.

問40　なぜ、悲しいと涙が出るの？

答　①眼の表面にはいつも、少量の涙で覆われています。②眼
が受ける刺激をやわらげ、眼を守るためです。③眼にごみが入
ったときや、眼の表面が刺激を受けたときにも涙が出ます。④こ
れらは三叉神経の働きによるものです。
　⑤悲しいときやうれしいときなどに出る涙は、刺激を受けたと
きに出る涙とは違います。⑥それは自律神経によるものです。
⑦自律神経は、交感神経と副交感神経に分かれています。⑧怒
りや悔しさなどの強い感情の昂ぶりを感じたときには、交感
神経のほうがよく働き、しょっぱい涙が少し出ます。⑨悲しい
ときや感動したときは、副交感神経のほうがよく働き、薄くて
水っぽい涙が大量に出ます。
　⑩涙にはプロラクチンや副腎皮質刺激ホルモンなど、ストレス
に反応して緊張を誘発する物質や、過剰になるとうつ病の原因
になるとされているマンガンが含まれています。⑪泣くとすっ
きりするのは、これらが涙とともに排出されるからだという説
もあります。

Q41 How can the tongue detect taste?

①The tongue can detect taste because taste buds,
舌　　　　　　味を検出する→味を感じる　　　味蕾
which behave as taste sensors, are distributed
　　　　　～として作用する　　　　　　　　～に分布している
on the tongue. ②There are about ten thousand taste buds

contained in the lingual papillae, small bump-like structures.
～に入っている　舌乳頭　　　　　　　　　　突起のようなもの
③When food touches the taste buds, this stimulus is transmitted
　　　　　　　　　　　　　　　　　　　　刺激　　　　伝えられる
to the brain and we detect taste. ④There are five taste modalities:
　　　　　　　　　　　　　　　　　　　　　　　　　　　味覚
sweet, sour, salty, bitter, and umami or savory. ⑤It had been
　　　　　　　　　　　　　　　　　　　　味のよいもの
thought that the four taste modalities except umami were detected
　　　　　　　　　　　　　　　　　　　　除いて
by different parts of the tongue until the 1990's. ⑥According to
　　　　　　　　　　　　　　　　　　　　　　　　　　　～によると
one of the theories, sweetness is detected by the tip of the
１つの説　　　　　　　　　　　　　　　　　　　　先
tongue, saltiness by the front sides of the tongue, sourness by the

back sides of the tongue and bitterness by the back of tongue.

⑦This diagram was called the tongue map.
　　　図
⑧Nowadays, this theory has been disproven and it is
　　　　　　　　　　　　　　　誤りであるとされている
accepted that one taste bud detects all five tastes. ⑨There is an
認められる
opening called a taste pore on top of a taste bud which contains
穴　　　　　　　味孔
the taste receptor cells. ⑩Each taste receptor cell is
味の受容細胞→味細胞

connected to a taste nerve. ⑪The chemical substances contained
　　　　　　味神経　　　　　　　　化学物質　　　　　　　　　　含まれる
in food enter through the taste pore which generates a stimulus
　　　　　　　　　　　　　　　　　　　　　　　　　生み出す　　刺激信号
signal, which is transmitted to the gustatory center in the cerebrum
　　　　　　　　　　　　　　　　　　　　味覚中枢　　　　　　　　大脳
and we detect taste. ⑫The widely accepted theory is that a taste
　　　　　　　　　　　　　広く受け入れられた説→有力な説
receptor cell receives only one modality of taste and transmits the

signal through the nerves specified for the taste to the brain.

問41　舌はどのように味を感じるの？

答 ①舌で味を感じるのは味のセンサーである味蕾が舌に分布しているからです。②舌の舌乳頭という小さな突起部分に、味蕾が1万個ほどあります。③食べ物が味蕾に接したときに、その刺激が脳に伝わることで、私たちは味を感じます。④味の種類は甘味、酸味、塩味、苦味、うま味の5つです。⑤1990年頃まで、うま味以外の4つの味は舌の異なった位置で感知されると考えられていました。⑥一つの説として、甘味を感知するのは舌先、塩味は舌の前方の両サイド、酸味は舌の奥の方の両サイド、苦味を感知するのは舌の奥というものがありました。⑦これが舌の味覚地図と呼ばれました。⑧現在、これは否定されており、1つの味蕾が五味をすべて感知するとされています。⑨1つの味蕾の上部には味孔という穴があり、その下に、複数の味細胞が集まっています。⑩それぞれの味細胞は味神経につながっています。⑪味孔から入った食べ物の化学物質が刺激信号となり、大脳の味覚中枢に伝わると味を感じます。⑫1つの味細胞は1種類の味だけを受容し、その味に特化した味神経につながって味を脳に伝えるという説が有力です。

Q42 Why does alcohol make people drunk?

①After you drink alcohol, your stomach and
アルコール (飲料)　　　　　　　胃
intestine take it in. ②Then alcohol gets into the
腸　　～を吸収する　　　　　　　　　　　　～に入る　　血液
blood and goes to the liver, where it is usually broken
　　　　　　　　　　肝臓　　　　　　　　　　　　　　　　分解される
down. ③However, some alcohol which is not broken down

and stays in the blood flows through blood vessels to the
　　～に留まる　　　　　　　～を通って流れる　　血管
brain. ④This alcohol paralyzes the brain little by little.
脳　　　　　　　　　　～を麻痺させる　　　　　徐々に
⑤This state is drunkenness.
　　　　　　　酔っぱらっていること
⑥As the blood-alcohol level goes up, the cerebral neocortex is
～するにつれて　血中アルコール濃度　　　　大脳新皮質
paralyzed and then the paralysis spreads to the cerebral limbic
　　　　　　　　　　　麻痺　　～に広がる　　大脳辺縁系
system, the cerebellum, the hippocampus, and finally to the
　　　　　　　小脳　　　　海馬
medulla oblongata. ⑦When only the cerebral neocortex is
延髄
paralyzed, you are slightly drunk and flush a little. ⑧When the
　　　　　　　　　　少し酔った　　　　　　顔が少し赤くなる
cerebellum is paralyzed, you become unsteady on your feet
　　　　　　　　　　　　　　　　　　　　足元がふらつく
and can not walk straight. ⑨You sometimes feel like vomiting
　　　　　　　まっすぐに　　　　　　　　　　吐き気を感じる
in this case. ⑩When the hippocampus, which is the center of
　　　　　　　　　　　　　　　　　　　　　　記憶中枢
the memory, is paralyzed, you can not speak well and you have

a poor memory. ⑪Finally, when the medulla oblongata is
乏しい記憶力

114

paralyzed, you can not move your body and you are in serious
非常に危険な状態で
danger.

⑫In the course of time, alcohol in the blood is broken down in
時間がたつにつれて
the liver. ⑬The brain recovers from the paralysis and you come
～から回復する　　　　　　　　　　正気に戻る
to yourself as this breaking down continues and the blood-
進む
alcohol level goes down. (see p.117)

問42　酒を飲むと、どうして酔っぱらうの？

答　①酒を飲むと、アルコール分はまず胃や腸で吸収されます。②続いて血液に入り肝臓へ送られ、分解されます。③肝臓で分解されなかったアルコールは、血液の中に残されたまま、血管を通り、脳に達します。④そして、脳を麻痺させていきます。⑤これが、酔っぱらった状態です。
⑥血液中のアルコール濃度が上がるにつれ、大脳新皮質→大脳辺縁系→小脳→海馬→延髄と麻痺が広がります。⑦大脳新皮質が麻痺している状態は、顔がほんのり赤くなるほろ酔い状態です。⑧小脳が麻痺すると足元がふらつき、まともに歩けなくなります。⑨吐き気を感じることもあります。⑩記憶中枢である海馬まで麻痺が進むと、ろれつがまわらなくなり、記憶が定かでなくなります。⑪そして、最後に延髄が麻痺すると、体を動かすことができなくなり、非常に危険な状態に陥ります。
⑫時間がたつにつれ、血液中のアルコールは肝臓で分解されていきます。⑬分解が進むと血液中のアルコール濃度が下がり、脳が麻痺から回復して酔いがさめます。

ヒトとサルは同じ祖先から枝分かれした

Human beings and chimpanzees separated from the common ancestor.

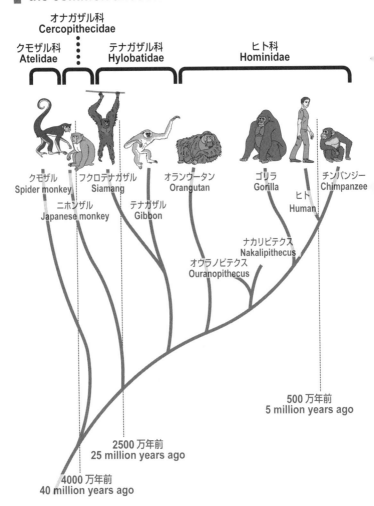

酒を飲むと、脳の麻痺が進むにつれて酔いが増す

When you drink alcohol, you feel drunk more as your brain becomes paralyzed.

ほろ酔い状態
Slight drunkenness

大脳新皮質が麻痺
The cerebral neo cortex is paralyzed.

顔がほんのり赤くなる
You flush a little.

千鳥足状態
Tipsy stagger

小脳が麻痺する
The cerebellum is paralyzed.

足元がふらつき、まともに歩けない
You become unsteady on your feet and can not walk straight.

酩酊状態
Heavy drunkenness

海馬が麻痺する
The hippocampus is paralyzed.

ろれつがまわらず、記憶が定かでない
You can not speak well and you have a poor memory.

昏睡状態
Coma

延髄が麻痺する
The medulla oblongata is paralyzed.

体を動かすことができない
You can not move your body.

Why are feces brown?

①What you eat goes from the mouth to the small
　　食べたもの　　　　　　　　　　　　　　　小腸
intestine by way of the gullet, the stomach, and
　　　　　　～を経て　　　食道　　　　　胃
the duodenum. ②Nutrients are taken in mainly at the small
十二指腸　　　　　栄養分　　　吸収される
intestine, and the rest such as food fiber is sent to the large
　　　　　　　　　残りもの　　　食物繊維　　　　　　　　大腸
intestine with water. ③At the large intestine, water is taken
in and the waste is excreted as feces.
　　　　排泄物　　　押し出される　ウンチとして
④The coloring matter of feces is bilirubin, which is in bile
　　色素　　　　　　　　　　　　　ビリルビン　　　　　　　胆汁
made in the liver. ⑤Bile is made in the liver and goes
　　　　肝臓　　　コレシスト　　　　　　　　　　　　　　　　　　～を通っていく
through the cholecyst and the bile duct to the duodenum,
　　　　　　胆嚢　　　　　　　胆管
where what you eat is mixed with bile.

⑥Bile acid is found in bile as well as bilirubin. ⑦Bile
　　胆汁酸　　　　　　　　　　　～と同様に
acid makes it easier to digest or take in fat. ⑧Bilirubin is
　　　　　　　　　　　～を消化する　　　　　脂肪
made from broken-down hemoglobins of old blood, which
　　　　　分解された　　　ヘモグロビン
is a kind of the waste. ⑨Bilirubin is also called
bile pigment, and it is yellow. ⑩The color of feces comes
胆汁色素
from the brown color of stercobilinogen, which is made from
　　　　　　　　　　　　ステルコビリノーゲン
bilirubin by intestinal bacteria, and the yellow color of
　　　　　　腸内細菌

bilirubin remained.
　　残りの

問43　ウンチはどうして、茶色なの？

答　①食べたものは口から食道、胃、十二指腸を経て小腸に送られます。②小腸などで栄養分が吸収され、繊維分（せんいぶん）などのカスが水分と一緒に大腸に送られます。③そして、大腸で水分が吸収されたものが、ウンチとなり、肛門から排出されるのです。④ウンチの色のもととなる色素は、肝臓でつくられる胆汁（たんじゅう）に含まれているビリルビンです。⑤胆汁は肝臓でつくられ、胆嚢（たんのう）、胆管を経て十二指腸に送られ、そこで食べたものと混じります。⑥胆汁には、ビリルビンのほかに胆汁酸が含まれています。⑦胆汁酸には、脂肪を消化・吸収しやすくする働きがあります。⑧ビリルビンは、古くなった血液のヘモグロビンが分解されたもので、一種の排泄物（はいせつぶつ）です。⑨胆汁色素とも呼ばれるもので、黄色をしています。⑩このビリルビンから腸内の細菌によってつくられるステルコビリノーゲンの褐色（かっしょく）と、残りのビリルビンの黄色がウンチの色となるのです。

Q44　Why do we dream?

①It is said that human beings dream mainly during
REM sleep (rapid eye movement sleep), or light
sleep. ②There are many hypotheses about why we
dream, but the mechanism of dreams has not been
clarified yet.

③The most popular hypothesis is that dreams have
something to do with a brain wave called the PGO wave
(Ponto-geniculo-occipital wave). ④It is known that the
brain sends out PGO waves during REM sleep. ⑤There is a
part of the brain which controls vision in the cerebral
cortex. ⑥The hypothesis says that this part of the brain,
stimulated by PGO waves, calls up visual images from
memories in fragments.

⑦PGO waves are sent out not only from the brain of human
beings but also from that of most other mammals during
sleep. ⑧If this theory is true, cats and dogs are very likely
to dream as well as human beings.

問44　人はなぜ、夢を見るの？

答 ①人間が夢を見るのは、主に眠りが浅いレム睡眠中だといわれています。②そのメカニズムについては、いくつかの説がありますが、はっきりとしたことはまだ解明されていません。③なかでも有力なのは、脳波の一種であるPGO波と関係しているという説です。④レム睡眠中には、PGO波が出ることが知られています。⑤大脳皮質には、視覚を司る部分があります。⑥レム睡眠中にPGO波がこの部分を刺激することにより、記憶の中から断片的に視覚的なイメージが呼び起こされたものだとする説です。

⑦PGO波は人間だけでなく、ほとんどの哺乳類が睡眠中に出すことが知られています。⑧この説が正しいとすると、人間だけではなく犬も猫も夢を見ている可能性が高くなります。

Q45 Why do we have fever, cough, and a sore throat when we catch cold?

①A cold is caused by disease agents such
　　　　　～によって引き起こされる　病原体

as germs and viruses. ②When these disease agents
　　　細菌　　　　ウイルス

enter the human body, the body tries to protect its
　　　　　人間の体　　　　　　　　　　　　　　～を—から守る

cells from the attack by them. ③This is what we call
細胞　　　　　攻撃　　　　　　　　　　　　　　　いわゆる

immune reaction.
免疫反応

④The first immune reaction is inflammation, which is the
　　　　　　　　　　　　　　　　　　　インフラメィション
　　　　　　　　　　　　　　　　　　　炎症

cause of coughs, sore throats, and so on. ⑤Today, it is made
原因　　コーフス　ソー　のどの痛み　　　　　　　　　　　　　～ということが知られている
　　　　せき

known that what causes inflammation is a protein generally
　　　　　　～するもの　　　　　　　　　　　タンパク質　　～と総称される

called inflammatory cytokine. ⑥It is made by white blood
　　　炎症性サイトカイン　　　　　　　　　　　　白血球

cells named macrophages, which play a part in fighting
　　　～と名づけられた　マクロファージ　　　　　～する役割を果たす　～と戦うこと

against the disease agents. ⑦Cytokines attract white blood
　　　　　　　　　　　　　　　　　　　　　　　～を呼び寄せる

cells by inflammation and coagulate blood and stop the
　　　　　　　　　　　　　　凝固させる　　　　　　　～に—させない

disease agents from spreading to other parts in order to
　　　　　　　from　～に広がること　　　　　　　　～するために

keep the sickness from getting worse.
～が—しないようにする　　悪くなること

⑧Cytokine plays a role in fever, one of the inflammation
　　　　　　　　　　　　　　発熱

reactions. ⑨When cytokines get to the brain, the
　　　　　　　　　　　　　　　　　　　脳

temperature control center orders the body to raise its
体温調節中枢　　　　　　　　　　～に―するように指令する　　　　　　～を上げる
temperature. ⑩Rise in body temperature keeps disease
　　　　　　　　　　～の上昇
agents from increasing and makes white blood cells work
　　　　　　　増殖すること　　　　　　　　　　　　活発に働くこと
actively, so the sickness is likely to be cured.
　　　　　　　　　　　　　　　　　　～しやすい　　治る

 風邪をひくと、なぜ熱やせきが出たり、のどが痛くなったりするの？

答 ①風邪の原因となるのは、細菌やウイルスなどの病原体です。②病原体が体内に入ると、人間の体はこれらの攻撃から細胞を守ろうとします。③いわゆる免疫反応です。
④免疫反応として最初に起こるのが、せきやのどの痛みなどの原因となる炎症です。⑤炎症を引き起こすのは、炎症性サイトカインと総称されるタンパク質であることが明らかになっています。⑥これは、病原体と戦う役割を持ったマクロファージと呼ばれる白血球によってつくり出されるものです。⑦炎症により、白血球を呼び寄せたり、血液を凝固させて病原体がほかの場所に広がるのを抑えたりして、病気の悪化を防ぎます。
⑧発熱という炎症反応にもサイトカインがかかわっています。⑨サイトカインが脳に達すると、体温調節中枢が体温を上げる指令を出します。⑩体温が上がることにより、病原菌の増殖が抑えられるとともに、白血球が活発に働き、病気が治りやすくなるからです。

①It is easy to understand that stomach medicine
　　　　　　　　　　　　　　　　　　　胃薬
can cure stomachaches because it dissolves in the
　　　ストマッケイクス
　　　～を治す 胃痛　　　　　　　　　　　　　　溶ける
stomach. ②Then, how does medicine work when we take it
　　　　　　　　それでは
for headaches?
　ヘッデエイクス
　　頭痛

③Medicine for headache such as aspirin dissolves in the
　　　　　　　　　　　　　　　アスピリン
stomach and enters the small intestine. ④After that, it gets
　　　　　　～へ吸収される 小腸　　　　　　　　　　　　　　～に入る
into the blood and goes to all parts of the body by way of
　　　血液　　　　　　　　　　　　　　　　　　　　　　　～を経て
the liver. ⑤Medicine for headaches gets to the head, the
肝臓
painful part, through blood vessels 15 to 30 minutes after
痛む部分　　　～を通って 血管　　　　～の15～30分後
taking the medicine.

⑥One of the causative agents of headache and period pain
　　　　　　原因物質　　　　　　　　　　　　　生理痛
is prostaglandin. ⑦It produces pain by stimulating the
　プロスタグランジン　　　痛みを引き起こす　刺激すること
nerves. ⑧Over-the-counter medicine for headaches such as
神経　　　市販薬
aspirin works to keep the prostaglandin from causing pain.
　　　　　　　　～が―しないようにする　　　　　～を引き起こすこと
⑨This effect eases pain.
　　　　　　　　～をやわらげる
⑩To sum up, medicine for headaches taken through the
　つまり　　　　　　　　　　　　　　　　口から服用された～

mouth enters the small intestine and is carried to all parts
　　　　　　　　　　　　　　　　　　　　～に運ばれる
of the body through blood vessels, and then it removes the
　　　　　　　　　　　　　　　　　　　　　　　　　　～を取り除く
cause of pain and the headache goes away.
　　　　　　　　　　　頭痛が治る

問46　口から飲んだ薬で、なぜ頭痛が治るの？

答　①胃薬を飲むと、薬が胃で溶けるため胃痛が治るのはわかります。②では、頭が痛いとき飲んだ薬はどのように効くのでしょうか。

③アスピリンに代表される頭痛薬は、胃で溶け、小腸で吸収されます。④その後、血液に入り、肝臓を経て全身に運ばれます。⑤頭痛薬は、服用後15〜30分程度で血流に乗って患部である頭部に到達します。

⑥頭痛や生理痛の原因の一つとして、プロスタグランジンという物質があげられます。⑦これが神経を刺激することにより、痛みが起こります。⑧アスピリンなど市販の頭痛薬には、プロスタグランジンが痛みを引き起こすことを妨げる作用があります。⑨この作用が、痛みをやわらげます。

⑩つまり、口から服用した頭痛薬が小腸から吸収され、血液によって患部に運ばれ、これが痛みの原因を取り除くため、頭痛が治るのです。

Why doesn't the stomach wall dissolve in stomach acid?

①Strong acid liquid and an enzyme that breaks down protein named pepsin come out in the stomach. ②The strong acid liquid and pepsin digest substances so strongly that they can break down meat. ③However, they do not digest the stomach itself, a muscular organ. ④Why not?

⑤The stomach wall is covered with mucous membranes which produce mucus. ⑥Mucus is made up mainly of mucin, which is the cause of stickiness in fishskin, taro, fermented soybeans, and so on.

⑦A mucous gel layer a few millimeters thick is on the surface of mucous membranes. ⑧The gel is something like konnyaku jelly or gelatin. ⑨When mucous membranes are broken down by strong acid liquid or pepsin on the surface of a gel layer, new mucous membranes take the place of the old ones. ⑩The reason why the stomach wall does not

126

dissolve in the strong acid liquid or the digestive enzyme is
〜に溶ける　　　　　　　　　　　　　消化酵素
that this gel layer protects the stomach.

問47　胃の壁はなぜ、胃酸で溶けないの？

答①胃の中には強い酸性の液とペプシンというタンパク質分解酵素があります。②これらには肉類も分解してしまうほど、強力な消化作用があります。③しかし、筋肉でできている胃自体は消化されることがありません。④これはなぜでしょうか？⑤胃の壁は粘膜で覆われ、粘液が出されています。⑥粘液の主成分はムチンと呼ばれるもので、魚の皮、サトイモ、納豆などのぬめりのもととなる物質です。

⑦粘膜の表面では、粘液が厚さ数ミリメートルのゲル層をつくっています。⑧ゲルというのは、コンニャクやゼラチンのような状態です。⑨ゲル層の表面で強い酸やペプシンにより粘液が分解されると、新しい粘液に置き換わるしくみが働いています。⑩胃の壁が強い酸や消化酵素の影響を受けないのは、このゲル層によって守られているからです。

Q48 Why does the head hurt after eating shaved ice?

①The headache you have after eating something
頭痛　　　　　　　　　　　　　　　　　何か冷たいもの
cold is called an ice cream headache. ②There
　　　　　　アイスクリーム頭痛
seem to be two ideas about why you get an ice cream
～であるようだ　　考え
headache.

③One of them is an idea which has something to do with
　　　　　　　　　　　　　　　　　　　　～と関係がある
nerve messages. ④When you eat something cold,
神経伝達
information that it is cold in the mouth is sent to the brain
情報　　　　　　　　　　　　　　口　　　～へ送られる 脳
through the trifacial nerve. ⑤The stimulus of ice cream and
　　　　三叉神経　　　　　　　　　刺激
ice, which are very cold, are so strong that information
　　　　　　　　　　　　　　とても～なので―
about nerves is confused and sent to the brain as
　　　　　　　　混乱する
information that the head hurts.
　　　　　　　　　　　痛む
⑥The other idea is that something cold causes inflammation
　　　　　　　　　　　　　　　　　　～を引き起こす 炎症
of the blood vessels. ⑦A reaction to try to increase blood
　　血管　　　　　　反応　　　　　　　～を増やす 血流
flow is caused to warm the inside of the mouth which is
　　　　　　　　　　～を温めるために
cooled down by the ice. ⑧As a result, this idea says the

blood vessels in the brain become inflamed temporarily
　　　　　　　　　　　　炎症を起こす　　　一時的な

128

because the blood vessels in the brain suddenly swell.
　　　　　　　　　　　　　　　　　　　　急に　　太くなる

問48　かき氷を食べると、なぜ頭痛がするの？

答　①冷たいものを食べたあとに起こる頭痛は、「アイスクリーム頭痛」と呼ばれています。②なぜ、アイスクリーム頭痛が起こるのかについては、二つの説があるようです。

③一つは、神経による伝達に関係があるとする説です。④冷たいものを食べると、「口の中が冷たい」という情報が三叉神経を経て脳に伝わります。⑤アイスクリームや氷は非常に冷たいため、その強烈な刺激によって神経の情報が混乱し、「頭が痛い」という情報として伝わってしまう、というものです。

⑥もう一つは、冷たいものが血管の炎症を引き起こすとする説です。⑦冷たくなった口の中を温めるため、血流を増やそうとする反応が起こります。⑧そこで、頭の血管が急激に太くなるため、頭の血管が一時的に炎症を起こす、という説です。

夢は、レム睡眠時に見ることが多い

You dream mainly during REM sleep (rapid eye movement sleep).

レム睡眠の状態
During REM sleep

筋肉はゆるんでいる
Muscles are relaxing.

眼球が動く
Your eyes move.

脳は覚醒時に近い状態
Your brain is nearly awake.

夢を見るしくみ
How you dream

視覚を司る部分
The part which controls vision

橋
Bridge

脳幹にある「橋」から出るPGO波が大脳皮質を刺激し、夢の視覚イメージが生まれる
The PGO waves the "bridge" in the brain stem gives off stimulate the cerebral cortex and call up visual pictures of the dream.

かき氷を食べると頭痛がするしくみは?

This is how you have headache after eating shaved ice.

① 強い刺激で、脳が混乱する

The strong stimulus causes information in the brain confused.

冷たいという強い刺激が三叉神経に伝わると、脳が混乱し、「痛い」という情報になる

When information that it is cold is sent to the trifacial nerve, the brain is confused and thinks of it as information that it hurts.

混乱!

Confusion!

三叉神経
The trifacial nerve

② 脳の血管が拡張する

The brain vessels swell.

血流を増やして冷えた口の中を温めるため、頭の血管が急に太くなり痛みを感じる

Blood flow is increased to warm the inside of the mouth and the brain vessels swell suddenly, so you feel pain.

血管が太くなり、神経を刺激する
The vessels swell and stimulate the nerves.

Q49   Why do you have white hair?

①There is a hair papilla at the base of a
　　　　　毛乳頭　　　　　　　　髪の毛のつけ根

hair. ②Hair matrix cells, which grow hairs, are
　　　　　　毛母細胞

around the hair papilla. ③Nutrients are sent to hair matrix
　　　　　　　　　　　　　　栄養分

cells through capillary vessels and the hair matrix cells
　　　　　　　　毛細血管

divide to grow a hair.
分裂して～する

④There are pigment cells called melanocyte around the
　　　　　色素細胞　　　　　　メラノサイト

hair papilla. ⑤Melanin pigment which is produced in the
　　　　　　　メラニン色素

melanocyte goes into the hair, so clear hair becomes black.
　　　　　　　　　　　　　　　　　透明な

⑥Hairs repeat the cycle of the anagen phase, catagen
　　　　～を繰り返す　～のサイクル　成長期　　　　　　退行期

phase, and telogen phase. ⑦The anagen phase lasts for
　　　　　休止期　　　　　　　　　　　　　　　　　　続く

three to six years and hair grows during this phase. ⑧The
　　　　　　　　　　　　　　　　　　　段階

catagen phase lasts for a few weeks and hair stop growing

during this phase. ⑨The telogen phase lasts for three to

four months, during which the hair falls out and the hair
　　　　　　　　　　　　　　　　　　抜ける

matrix cells get ready to grow new hair.
　　　　～する準備をする

⑩In the telogen phase, you lose melanocyte with your hair.

⑪If you are young and have energy, melanocyte is
　　　　　　　　　　　　　　　元気

132

produced to grow new hair and is placed around the hair
　　　　　　　　　　　　　　　　　　　　　　　　配置される
papilla. ⑫However, you have white hair when the

melanocyte is not properly placed and the hair is not filled
　　　　　　　　　　　　　　　　　　　　　　　　　　～で満たされる
with it because of sickness, aging, stress, and so on.
　　　　　　　　　　　　　　　加齢　　ストレス

問49　なぜ、白髪になるの？

答 ①髪の毛のつけ根の部分には毛乳頭（もうにゅうとう）があります。②その
まわりに、毛髪をつくる毛母細胞（もうぼ）があります。③毛細血管によ
り養分が運ばれ、毛母細胞が細胞分裂をして毛髪をつくります。
④毛乳頭の周辺には、メラノサイトという色素細胞があります。
⑤メラノサイトでつくられたメラニン色素が毛髪に入るため、
透明だった毛髪が黒くなります。
⑥髪の毛は成長期→退行期→休止期というサイクルを繰り返して
います。⑦成長期は３〜６年間で、この間に髪の毛が伸びます。
⑧退行期は２〜３週間で、髪の毛の成長が止まります。⑨休止期
は３〜４ヵ月で、脱毛の後、毛母細胞が次の発毛の準備をします。
⑩休止期に脱毛するときには、毛髪とともにメラノサイトが失
われます。⑪若くて元気なら、再び発毛するときにメラノサイ
トが作られ、毛乳頭の周辺に配置されます。⑫しかし、病気や
加齢、ストレスなどによりメラノサイトがうまく配置されなく
なると、髪の毛にメラニン色素がいき渡らなくなるので、白髪
になります。

Q50 Where do baby's feces go in the mother's body?

①A baby in its mother's body <u>spends about 9 months floating</u> in <u>amniotic fluid</u> in her <u>womb</u>.
~して過ごす　　　　　　羊水　　　　　　　　　子宮

②The baby gets <u>nutrients</u> and <u>oxygen</u> from the mother through the <u>umbilical cord</u>.
栄養素　　　　酸素　　　　　　　へその緒

③The baby in its mother's body doesn't eat <u>anything</u>, so it <u>has no feces</u>.
何も（～ない）　　ウンチをしない

④The baby drinks amniotic fluid through its mouth and <u>urinates back into</u> amniotic fluid.
~におしっこをする

⑤<u>During this period</u>, the baby <u>keeps wastes</u>, such as <u>pieces of skin</u>, hair, and so on, in <u>its intestine</u>.
この間に　　　　　　　　　　　~をためる　不要物　　　皮膚の破片　　　　　　　自分の腸

⑥The first feces the baby <u>excretes</u> <u>after birth</u> are called <u>meconium</u>.
排泄する　生まれたあと　　　　胎便

⑦Meconium is the waste of amniotic fluid kept for 9 months and it has a <u>dark color</u> and little smell.
暗い色

⑧When the baby stays in its mother's body <u>even after the expected date of its birth</u>, the <u>placenta</u> doesn't work well
出産予定日　　　　　~のあとでも　胎盤

and the baby <u>has discomfort</u> and feces float in amnionic fluid.
不快に感じる

⑨If the feces go into the baby's <u>lung</u> <u>through the throat</u>, the baby sometimes <u>has difficulty breathing</u> and it
肺　　気管を通って　　　　　　呼吸するのが困難になる

gets into danger.
危険になる

⑩If it takes too long for the baby to excrete meconium after
　～が一するのに一かかる

birth, the baby is likely to be jaundiced because the
　　　　　　　～になりやすい　　　黄疸になる　ジョーンディスト

bilirubin, yellow coloring matter in the meconium gets into
ビリルビン　黄色の色素　　　　　　　　　　　　　　　　　　～に入る

the blood again from the intestine.

問50 お腹の中の赤ちゃんのウンチは、どうなっているの？

答 ①赤ちゃんはお母さんのお腹の中で、子宮の中の羊水に浮かんで約9ヵ月間過ごします。②赤ちゃんはお母さんからへその緒を通じて栄養と酸素をもらいます。③食べ物を食べるわけではないのでウンチはしません。④口から羊水を飲んで、おしっこをまた羊水の中に戻します。⑤そのときに羊水に含まれる皮膚や毛などのゴミを、自分の腸の中にためておきます。⑥生まれてから初めて排泄するウンチを胎便といいます。⑦それは、9ヵ月の間にたまった羊水のゴミなどで、色が黒っぽくて臭いはあまりありません。

⑧出産予定日が過ぎてしまうと、胎盤の機能が低下し赤ちゃんが苦しくなって、羊水の中で胎便が出てしまうことがあります。⑨これが赤ちゃんの気管から肺に入ると、出産後に呼吸障害を起こすことがあり、危険です。

⑩また、生まれてから胎便が出るまでに時間がかかると、胎便に含まれる黄色の色素のビリルビンが腸管から血中へ再吸収されるので、黄疸になりやすくなります。

Q51 Why don't human beings breathe in water?

①Mammals such as human beings breathe with the lungs. ②There are many small bags named air sacs and they contain a lot of capillary vessels are in them. ③Air taken in through breathing goes through the throat and eventually reaches the air sacs. ④There, the air is taken in by blood flowing through the capillary vessels and, at the same time, carbon dioxide and water are exuded. ⑤This system does not work in water. ⑥Imagine that you take in water instead of air. ⑦When air sacs are filled with water, oxygen can not be exchanged for carbon dioxide in the blood. ⑧Furthermore, water goes into your blood when you take in pure water and water in blood comes out when you take in sea water, so the balance in the blood is lost in either case. ⑨This causes death.

⑩The baby in mother's body can live in amniotic fluid because it does not breathe with the lung but it gets oxygen

from the mother and releases carbon dioxide to the mother
through the placenta.
　　　　　　　　胎盤

問51　人はどうして、水の中で息ができないの？

答　①人間をはじめとする哺乳類は肺で呼吸します。②肺の中には肺胞という無数の小さな袋があり、毛細血管が集まっています。③呼吸することによって取り込まれた空気は、気管を通り最終的に肺胞に送られます。④そこで、毛細血管を流れる血液に酸素が取り込まれ、同時に二酸化炭素や水分が排出されます。

⑤このしくみは、水中では通用しません。⑥仮に空気の代わりに水を吸い込んだとしましょう。⑦肺胞が水で満たされると、血液の酸素と二酸化炭素の交換ができなくなります。⑧さらに、水の場合は浸透圧によって水が血液中に入り、海水の場合は逆に血液中の水分が流出して、血液のバランスが崩れてしまいます。⑨これは人間にとって死を意味します。

⑩胎児が羊水の中で生きていられるのは、肺で呼吸せず、胎盤を通して母親から酸素をもらい、二酸化炭素を戻しているからです。

Q52 How do you find a criminal by a fingerprint?

①There are no pores at the tip of a finger but
　　　　　　　毛穴　　　　　指先
there are sweat glands. ②The open mouths of the
　　　　　　汗腺　　　　　　開口部
sweat glands are raised and they form a pattern of
　　　　　　盛り上がっている　　　～を形成する　模様
equal-spaced ridges like a contour map. ③This is the
等間隔の隆線　　　　　　　　等高線図
fingerprint.
指紋

④The pattern of a fingerprint never changes from the

cradle to the grave. ⑤Even if you chip off the skin of the tip
ゆりかごから墓場まで(→一生)　～だとしても　～をはぎ取る
of your finger, the renewed tip has the same pattern of
　　　　　　　　　再生した　　　　　前と同じ～
fingerprint as before. ⑥It is true that the finger grows
　　　　　　　　　　　　確かに～だが　　　　　　　太くなる
thicker and the fingerprint grow bigger as people grow up
　　　　　　　　　　　　　　　　　　　　～につれて
but the pattern of the fingerprint never changes.

⑦There is no other person that has the same fingerprint as

you in the world. ⑧You can not tell the difference between
　　　　　　　　　　　　　　　　　　～を区別する
identical twins by DNA test but you can tell by their
一卵性双生児　　　　DNA鑑定
fingerprints. ⑨However, the fingerprints of identical twins

are not completely different. ⑩They have similar patterns
　　　完全に～というわけではない　　　　　　似た

of fingerprint because they have same genes but there is
遺伝子

difference enough to tell one from the other.
一方と他方を区別する

問52　指紋でなぜ、犯人が見つかるの？

答 ①指先には毛穴（けあな）はありませんが、汗腺（かんせん）があります。②汗腺の開口部は隆起（りゅうき）し、等高線のように一定間隔の隆線（りゅうせん）という模様をつくります。③これが指紋（しもん）です。

④指紋は、一生変わりません。⑤たとえ指先の皮膚（ひふ）をはぎ取っても、皮膚ができると同じ指紋になります。⑥子どもから大人に成長すると指が太くなり、指紋も大きくなりますが、パターンは変化しません。

⑦また、世の中に同じ指紋の人は存在しません。⑧ＤＮＡ鑑定で区別できない一卵性双生児も、指紋鑑定なら特定することができるのです。⑨ただし、一卵性双生児の指紋はまったく異なっているわけでもありません。⑩遺伝子が同一であるために指紋も似たパターンですが、指紋認証で区別できるほどの違いはあります。

Q53 Why don't we see things double though we have two eyes?

①We have two eyes, but we do not see things double. ②Why don't we see double?
ものが二つに見える

③There is a crystal lens in our eye. ④Light passing through
水晶体　　　　　　　　　　　　　　　　　～を通過する―

the crystal lens strikes the retina at the back of the eyeball.
～にあたる　網膜　　　～の奥にある　　眼球

⑤The image the retina receives is changed into signals by
像　　　　　　　　受け取る　　～に変換される　信号

the nerves in the eyes lining up on the retina, and the
視神経　　　　　　　　～の上に並ぶ

signals travel to the cerebrum as two images on the right
～に伝わる　大脳　　　　　　　　　　　　左右にある

and the left.

⑥The two images which travel as the signals through the
～として

nerve to the cerebrum from the right eye and the left eye are

overlapped by the following three functions of the cerebrum.
重ね合わせられる　　　　次の　　サイマルテニアス　機能

⑦The first one is simultaneous perception, which is a
同時視

function allowing us to see two different images at the same

time. ⑧The second is the fusion, which is a function which
融像

allows two images to overlap and make them into one.
　　　　　　　　　　　　　～を一つにする

⑨The third is binocular vision, which is a function which
　　　　　　ビノキュラー
　　　　　　立体視

creates a feeling of <u>distance and depth</u> by small differences
　　　　　　　　　　距離と立体の感覚

between the two images on the right and the left.

⑩Images <u>produced on</u> the retinas of the two eyeballs <u>come</u>
　　　　　〜の上に作られた　　　　　　　　　　　　　　　一緒になる

<u>together</u> because of these three functions of the cerebrum.

⑪<u>That is why</u> we can see things <u>in 3D</u>. (see p.144)
　　そのため　　　　　　　　　　　立体的に

問53　眼は二つあるのに、なぜものが一つに見えるの？

答　①私たちには眼が二つありますが、見えている像は一つ
だけです。②これは、なぜでしょうか？
③眼には水晶体というレンズがあります。④水晶体を通過した
光は、眼の一番奥にある網膜に映し出されます。⑤映し出され
た像は、両眼の網膜に並ぶ視神経によって信号に変換され、左
右二つの像として大脳に伝えられます。
⑥大脳に備わっている次の三つの働きによって、右眼と左眼か
ら神経を通じて信号として送られてきた二つの像が重ね合わせ
られます。⑦まず、「同時視」は、二つの異なった像を同時に
見る働きです。⑧次に、「融像」は二つの像を重ね合わせ、一
つの像にする働きです。⑨そして、「立体視」は、左右の像の
微妙な違いから、像に遠近感や立体感を与えます。
⑩大脳が持つ、これら三つの働きにより、二つの眼に映し出さ
れた像は一つになります。⑪そして、私たちは立体的にものを
見ることができるのです。

Why can you see clearly with glasses?

①The human eye is like a convex lens. ②The
　　　　人間の眼　　　　　　　　　凸レンズ
focal distance changes according to the thickness
焦点距離　　　　　　　～によって　　厚さ
of the lens. ③You usually move a magnifying glass back
　　　　　　　　　　　　　　　　　　虫眼鏡　　　　　　　前後に
and forth when you look at something small through it to
　　　　　　　　　　　　　　　　小さいもの
adjust the distance between the thing you want to see and
～の距離が―と等しくなるように調節するために
your eyes equal to the focal distance.

④You can not bring your eye into focus by adjusting the
　　　　　　　　　～の焦点を合わせる　　　　～を調整することで
distance between the crystal lens and the retina, which
　　　　　　　　　　水晶体　　　　　　　　網膜
receives images made by the light passing through the
　　　　　像　　　　　　　　　　　～を通過する―
crystal lens, because the distance between the lens and the
retina can not be changed in the eye. ⑤Therefore you adjust
　　　　　　　　　　　　　　　　　　そこで
the focal distance by changing the thickness of the crystal
lens by the power of a muscle in the ciliary body.
　　　　　　筋肉の力によって　　　　　　　毛様体
⑥A near sighted person can not focus on a distant thing
　　　近視の人　　　　　　　　　焦点を合わせる 遠くのもの
because he or she can not make the crystal lens thin.
　　　　　　　　　　　　　　　　　　　　　　　　薄い
⑦When the person sees through the glasses of a concave
　　　　　　　　　　　　　　　　　　　　　　　　凹レンズ

lens, he or she can see a distant thing clearly because this is
はっきりと

in the same state as it is when he or she makes the crystal
〜であるのと同じ状態で

lens, the convex lens, thin.

⑧On the other hand, a far sighted person wears glasses
遠視の人

with a convex lens because the lens of his or her eye is the
〜と反対に

opposite of that of a near sighted person. (see p.145)

(see p.145)

問54　メガネをかけると、なぜよく見えるようになるの？

答 ①人間の眼は凸レンズのようなものです。②レンズは厚さによって焦点距離も変わります。③虫眼鏡で小さいものを見るときレンズの位置を調節するのは、見る対象と眼の位置をレンズの焦点距離に合わせるためです。

④人間の眼は、レンズである水晶体とレンズを通過した光が像を結ぶ網膜が一体化しているため、それらの距離を調整してピントを合わせることができません。⑤そこで、毛様体の中にある筋肉の力で水晶体の厚さを変えて、焦点距離を調整します。

⑥近視の人は、水晶体を薄くできないため、遠くに焦点を合わせられません。⑦凹レンズのメガネをかけると、水晶体の凸レンズを薄くしたのと同じ状態になり、遠くもはっきり見えるようになります。

⑧一方、遠視の人は近視の人と逆の状態なので、凸レンズのメガネをかけます。

眼は二つあるのに、なぜものは一つに見えるの?

Why don't we see things double though we have two eyes?

視神経
Nerves in the eyes

大脳
Cerebrum

同時視
Simultaneous perception

両眼の像を同時に認識する
Sensing images at both eyes at the same time

融像
Fusion

両眼の像を重ね合わせる
Overlapping images at both eyes

立体視
Binocular vision

奥行きや立体感を認識する
Feeling distance and depth

メガネは水晶体の焦点を補正する
Glasses correct the focus of the crystal lens.

正常な眼
Good eye

眼のレンズである水晶体の焦点が網膜上にあるので、光は網膜にはっきりと像を結ぶ

Light makes images on the retina clearly because crystal lens, the lens in the eye, has a focal point on the retina.

近視
Near sight

水晶体を薄くできないので、焦点が網膜よりも手前になる

They cannot make the crystal lens thin so the focal point is before the retina.

凹レンズで焦点を後ろにずらすと、はっきりと見えるようになる

They can make the focal point far with a concave lens and see clearly.

遠視
Far sight

水晶体を厚くできないので、焦点が網膜よりも奥になる

They cannot make the crystal lens thick so the focal point is after the retina.

凸レンズで焦点を手前にずらすと、はっきりと見えるようになる

They can make the focal point near with a convex lens and see clearly.

Q 55

How do they check
the blood types, A, B, O, and AB?

①Human blood is classified into four types, A, B, O, and AB. ②They are determined by the red blood cells and protein in blood serum. ③When you mix two different types of blood, you can find that some pairs clot and others do not clot.

④Red blood cells in blood have A antigens or B antigens in them. ⑤A person with A type blood has A antigen and a person with B type blood has a B antigen. ⑥A person with O type blood has neither of them and a person who has both of them is one with AB type blood.

⑦Blood serum, the liquid portion of blood, has two kinds of antibodies, α and β, which make red blood cells together in reaction to the A antigen or the B antigen. ⑧A person with A type blood has β and a person with B type blood has α. ⑨A person with O type blood has both of them. ⑩A person with AB type blood has neither of them.

⑪When you mix two different types of blood, some pairs clot and others do not clot and you can determine the blood type.

問55　どうやって、Ａ、Ｂ、Ｏ、ＡＢの血液型を調べるの？

答　①人はＡ、Ｂ、Ｏ、ＡＢの４つの血液型のどれかに分類されます。②それは赤血球と血清の中のタンパク質で決まっています。③血液を混ぜ合わせてみると、固まる組み合わせと固まらない組み合わせがあることがわかります。

④血液の中の赤血球には、Ａ抗原またはＢ抗原が含まれています。⑤Ａ型の人はＡ抗原、Ｂ型の人はＢ抗原を持っています。⑥Ｏ型の人はどちらの抗原も持っていない人で、両方の抗原を持っている人はＡＢ型です。

⑦血液の液体成分である血清にはＡ、Ｂそれぞれの抗原に反応して赤血球を凝集させる物質である、二種類の抗体αとβが含まれています。⑧Ａ型の人はβを、Ｂ型の人はαを持っています。⑨Ｏ型の人は両方の抗体を持っています。⑩ＡＢ型の人はどちらの抗体も持っていません。

⑪混ぜ合わせたときの凝集の様子から血液型を特定するのです。

人の体はこんなに神秘的!

How mysterious human body is!

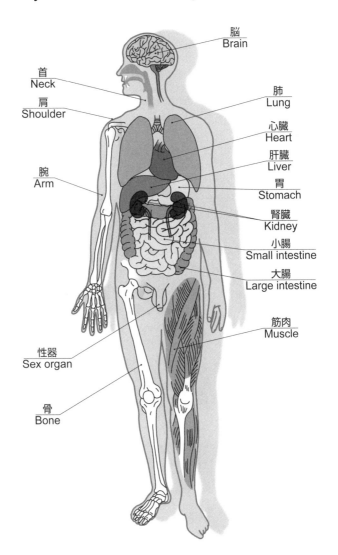

脳
Brain

首
Neck

肩
Shoulder

腕
Arm

肺
Lung

心臓
Heart

肝臓
Liver

胃
Stomach

腎臓
Kidney

小腸
Small intestine

大腸
Large intestine

筋肉
Muscle

性器
Sex organ

骨
Bone

Questions about the things around us

第5章

身の周りの疑問

Q56 Why can microwave ovens heat up food?

①There is an antenna-like thing, called a
アンテナのようなもの
magnetron, in the microwave ovens which gives
マグネトロン　　　　電子レンジ　　　　　　　　　〜を出す
off microwaves.
マイクロ波

②Any food has a lot of water molecules in it. ③A water
どんな食べ物も　　　　　　　水の分子
molecule is made up of two positively charged hydrogen
〜で構成される　　　　プラスの電気を帯びた　水素原子
atoms and one negatively charged oxygen atom. ④When a
　　　　　　　マイナスの電気を帯びた　酸素原子
microwave hits the water molecules, they vibrate and their
　　　　　　　　　　　　　　　　　　　　　　　振動する
temperature goes up because of friction. ⑤That is why food
その温度　　　　　　　　摩擦のために　　　　　そういうわけで
will be heated. ⑥Microwaves from this kind of oven
温められる
pass through dishes, which have no water in them, so
〜を通り抜ける　食器
dishes will not be heated. ⑦Therefore only food, which has

water in it, will be heated and become hot.

⑧The number of times an electric wave vibrates is called
回数　　　　　　　　　　電波
frequency. ⑨The microwaves from this oven have a
周波数
frequency of 2,450 megahertz, and positive charges and
周波数2450メガヘルツ　　　　　　　　　　　電荷
negative charges alternate with each other 2.45 billon
　　　　　　　　入れ替わる　　　　　　　　24億5000万回

times per second. ⑩This frequency is suitable for

1秒間に　　　　　　　　　　　　　　　〜するのに適している

vibrating water molecules and heating food. (See p.162)

温める

問56　電子レンジでどうして、料理が温まるの？

答 ①電子レンジは内部に「マグネトロン」というアンテナのようなものが設置されていて、ここからマイクロ波という電波を出します。

②食べ物にはたくさんの水の分子が含まれています。③水の分子は、プラスの電気を帯びた水素原子が2個とマイナスの電気を帯びた酸素原子が1個からできています。④マイクロ波を水の分子に当てると、揺さぶられて摩擦熱が生じて温度が上がります。⑤その結果、食べ物が温められます。⑥電子レンジのマイクロ波は水分を含まない食器を、通り抜けるので温まりません。⑦そのため、水分を含む食べものだけ、発熱して温まります。

⑧電波が振動する回数を「周波数」といいます。⑨電子レンジのマイクロ波の周波数は2450メガヘルツで、1秒間に24億5000万回、プラスとマイナスが交互に入れ替わります。⑩この周波数が、水の分子を振動させ食品の内部まで温めるのに適しているのです。

Q57 Why do eggs get hard when they are boiled?

①Eggs get hard when they are boiled. ②The hardness changes according to temperature and time: soft-boiled eggs, hard-boiled eggs, and hot-spring boiled eggs. ③This is because eggs have protein in them. ④A medium-sized egg which weighs around 50 grams has about 6 grams of protein. ⑤Albumin, which makes up more than half of the protein in the white, and lipoprotein, which is in the yolk, are both proteins but their natures are different.

⑥The white starts to get hard at 60 degrees C and becomes soft-boiled at about 65 degrees C. ⑦Then, it becomes hard-boiled at nearly 80 degrees C. ⑧On the other hand, the yolk becomes hard-boiled when the temperature is kept at around 65 to 70 degrees C.

⑨Hot-spring boiled eggs are made by taking advantage of this difference between the natures of these two kinds of

protein. ⑩When you keep the temperature of a raw egg at
　　　　　　　　　　　　　　　　　　　　　生卵
about 70 degrees C for about 20 minutes, it becomes a hot-

spring boiled egg, whose white is softer than its yolk.
　　　　　　　　　　　　　　　　～よりも柔らかい

問57　卵はどうして、ゆでると固くなるの？

答　①卵をゆでると、固くなります。②温度と時間を変える
と「半熟卵」、「固ゆで卵」、「温泉卵」と、固さも変化します。③こ
れは、卵がタンパク質を含んでいるからです。

④卵に含まれるタンパク質は、中ぐらいのもの1個（約50グ
ラム）につき、約6グラム程度です。⑤そして、卵白に含ま
れているタンパク質の半分以上を占めるアルブミンと卵黄に
含まれるリポタンパク質は、同じタンパク質でありながら異な
る性質を持っています。

⑥卵白は約60度で固まり始め、およそ65度で半熟になります。
⑦さらに、80度に近くになると固まります。⑧一方、黄身は
約65度から70度くらいに保つと、完全に固まります。

⑨こうした2つのタンパク質の性質の違いを利用してつくるの
が、温泉卵です。⑩生卵をおよそ70度の温度で20分程度保
温することにより、卵黄よりも卵白が柔らかい、温泉卵になる
のです。

Q58 Why does plastic cling film stick to something?

①Plastic cling film has no glue on it. ②However,
　　　ラップ　　　　　　　　　　糊
it sticks close to a plate or similar things.
　　～にぴったりとくっつく　皿
③Why can it do so?

④One of the reasons is that plastic cling film sticks close to

something hard such as a plate because it is very thin and
硬いもの　　　　　　　　　　　　　　　　　　　　　　　　　　薄い
soft.
柔らかい
⑤When one molecule gets close to another molecule, they
　　　　　　分子　　　～に近づく
try to pull each other and stick to together. ⑥This is
　　　～を引く　　　　　　　　　～にくっつく
called intermolecular force. ⑦Even when two paper boxes
　　　分子間力　　　　　　　　　～のときでさえも
are stacked, this force works between molecules that are
重なっている
close to each other, but it is very weak because of
互いに接近した
the uneven surface.
でこぼこの(凹凸がある)表面
⑧Thin plastic cling film made from soft material sticks to
　　　　　　　　　　　　　　　　　　　　　　　　素材
the rim of a plate or a cup. ⑨It sticks to the plate because
ふち
of the intermolecular force.

問58　ラップはなぜ、ぴったりくっつくの？

答　①ラップには糊はついていません。②にもかかわらず、お皿などにぴったりと密着させることができます。③これは、なぜでしょうか？

④その理由の一つとして、ラップが薄くて柔らかく、食器のような硬いものにぴったりと密着することがあげられます。

⑤ものの分子と分子が近づくと、お互いにくっつこうとする力が働きます。⑥「分子間力」と呼ばれるものです。⑦紙の箱を二つ重ねたときにも、接近した分子の間でこの力が働きますが、表面に凹凸があるため非常に弱いものです。

⑧柔らかい素材でできた薄いラップは、食器のふちに密着します。⑨その部分に分子間力が働くため、食器にぴったりとくっつくのです。

Q59 Why do tears come in your eyes when you slice an onion?

①If you put an unsliced whole onion close to
~を一に近づける　丸ごとのタマネギ
your eyes, tears do not come to your eyes.
涙　　　　　　　　眼に出る
②However, when you slice an onion, it stings your eyes and
~を刻む　　　　　~にしみる
you shed tears. ③Why does this happen?
涙を流す
④Onions have an element, isoalliin, in them. ⑤Isoalliin
成分　　　　　イソアリイン
does not become volatile at room temperature and it does
揮発する　　　　常温で
not sting your eyes. ⑥When you slice an onion, isoalliin

changes into thiosulfinate because of an enzyme called
~に変わる　　チオスルフィネート　　　　　　　　　エンザイム
酵素
alliinase. ⑦In an unsliced onion, isoalliin and alliinase are
アリナーゼ
in different cells, so they do not bind with each other.
異なった細胞に　　　　　　　　　　結合する
⑧When you slice an onion, these cells are broken and these

two elements change into thiosulfinate. ⑨Thiosulfinate is

irritating and is likely to become volatile. ⑩This element
刺激する　　　~しやすい
gets into your eyes and you shed tears.
~に入る

問59　タマネギを刻むと、どうして涙が出るの？

答 ①切っていない、丸ごとのタマネギを眼に近づけても、涙が出るということはありません。②ところが、タマネギを刻むと眼にしみて、涙が出てきます。③これは、なぜでしょうか？④タマネギにはイソアリインという成分が含まれています。⑤イソアリインは揮発性がなく、眼にしみることはありません。⑥タマネギを刻むとアリナーゼという酵素の働きで、イソアリインがチオスルフィネートに変化します。⑦刻まない状態のタマネギでは、イソアリインとアリナーゼは別の細胞にあり、混ざることはありません。⑧刻むことによって細胞が壊れ、この二つが混じってチオスルフィネートができるのです。⑨チオスルフィネートは刺激性があり、揮発しやすい性質があります。⑩これが眼に入ることによって、涙が出るのです。

Q60 Why does food go bad?

①Food goes bad because organic matters, especially protein, in it are broken down by bacteria called putrid bacteria and other microorganisms. ②There is a lot of bacteria in the air. ③There is also a lot of bacteria on your hands. ④When these bacteria transfer to food, they began to grow. ⑤Food for human beings is so nutritious for bacteria that they can easily grow in it. ⑥When these bacteria break down protein in the food, it gives off smelly gases such as ammonia and hydrogen sulfide. ⑦Some kinds of bacteria make toxins which cause food poisoning. ⑧This state is when you say meat or fish is bad.

⑨Rice and bread, which have almost no protein in them, sometimes go bad too. ⑩This is caused mainly by bacteria called grass bacilli. ⑪The grass bacilli are related to bacillus subtilis and they are everywhere. ⑫Even when rice goes bad by these bacteria, the rice does not have a very

bad smell and these bacteria do not make many toxins.
<u>におい</u> <u>あまり〜しない</u>

問60　食べ物はなぜ、腐るの？

答 ①「食べ物が腐る」のは、食べ物の中の有機物、特にタンパク質が腐敗菌と呼ばれる細菌やその他の微生物によって分解されるからです。

②空気中には、細菌が漂っています。③また、人間の手にも多くの細菌がついています。④これらが食べ物につくと、繁殖を始めます。⑤人間の食べ物は、細菌にとっても栄養が豊かで繁殖しやすい場所だからです。⑥これらが食べ物の中のタンパク質を分解すると、アンモニアや硫化水素など、悪臭の原因になるガスを出します。⑦菌の種類によっては、食中毒の原因となる毒素を出すこともあります。⑧これが、肉や魚などが腐った状態です。

⑨タンパク質をほとんど含まないご飯やパンが腐ることもあります。⑩その原因となるのは、主に枯草菌という細菌です。⑪納豆菌の仲間である枯草菌は、ごくありふれた細菌です。⑫この菌でご飯が腐敗しても、極端な悪臭や毒素を出すことはあまりありません。

Q61　Why is a drainpipe s-shaped?

①The drainpipes under the washstand, the
ドレインパイプス
配水管　　　　　　　　　　　洗面台

kitchen sink, and so on are S-shaped so that water
台所の流し　　　　　　　　　S字型である　　〜するように

is always standing at their curve. ②It is true that there are
〜にたまる　　　　　曲線　　　確かに〜だが,─

various shapes but all drainpipes are designed to keep
さまざまな　　　　　　　　　　　　〜するように設計されている

some water in the middle of them in this way. ③The water
このように

kept there is called seal water and it seals the drainpipe to
封水　　　　　　　〜をふさぐ

keep away smells and bugs. ④This system is called a trap.
〜を遠ざけておく においと虫　　　仕掛け　　　　トラップ

⑤Even if there is a trap in a drainpipe, it does not work
〜だとしても

when you let a large amount of water flow at one time
大量の水を流す　　　　　　　一度に

and there is no seal water. ⑥This is a phenomenon called
現象

self-siphon.
自己サイフォン

⑦Siphon is a system that can fill a curved pipe with liquid
〜を─で満たす 曲がった管　　　液体

and lead the liquid to the end point at a lower level than the
〜を─へ導く　　　終点　　〜より低い位置にある

starting point by way of a point at a higher level than the
出発点　　　〜を経由して

starting point. ⑧When you let a large amount of water flow

at one time, the drainpipe and trap work as a siphon and
〜として働く

the seal water drains away. (see p.163)
流れ出す

問61　　排水管の形はなぜ、S字型なの？

答　①たとえば、洗面所や台所などの下の配水管はS字に曲がっていて、常に水がたまるようになっています。②形はさまざまですが、排水設備には必ずこのように、途中に水をためておく仕掛けがあります。③たまっている水は「封水」と呼ばれ、排水経路をふさいで臭いや虫などの進入を防ぎます。④この仕掛けは、トラップと呼ばれています。

⑤せっかくトラップがついていても、大量の水を一気に流すと水がなくなり、効かなくなることがあります。⑥これは「自己サイフォン」と呼ばれる現象です。

⑦サイフォンとは、曲がった管の中で液体が途切れないようにして、ある地点から高い地点を越え、出発点より低い終点まで液体を導くようなしくみです。⑧大量の水を流すと、配水管とトラップがサイフォンの状態になり、たまった封水が流れ出てしまうのです。

電子レンジはマイクロ波で、食べ物の水分子を振動させて温める

The microwave oven vibrates and heats water molecules in food with a microwave.

マグネトロン
Magnetron

マイクロ波
Microwave

電子レンジでは、マグネトロンからマイクロ波を出している
Magnetron in the microwave oven gives off a microwave.

マイクロ波
Microwave

マイクロ波が食べ物の水分子を振動させる
Microwave vibrates water molecules in food.

水分子の振動で摩擦熱が生じ、食べ物が温まる
Heat is caused by the friction of water molecules and food is heated.

排水口に大量の水を流してはいけない理由

Why you mustn't let flow a large amount of water in the drainpipe at one time

悪臭
Bad smell

封水
Seal water

S字部分にたまった水が、下水から流れ込んでくる悪臭を遮断している
The water kept at S-shaped pipe keeps away bad smell from the sewer.

大量の水を一気に流すと……
When you let flow a large amount of water at one time …

たまった水が、途切れることなく押し出される
The water kept there all flows away.

サイフォンの効果で、S字部分にたまっていた封水まで、流れ出してしまう
Water kept at S-shaped pipe also flows away by siphon effect.

Q62　What is the real color of shrimp?

①The striped pattern of shrimp in a fish shop is
縞模様　　　　　　　　　エビ

blackish. ②However, the striped pattern of boiled
黒っぽい　　　　　　　　　　　　　　　　　　　　ゆでられた

shrimp on the table is reddish. ③Why do they differ?
赤っぽい　　　　　　　　異なる

④Boiled shrimp look red because they have a red coloring
　　　　　　　look　〜に見える　　　　　　　　　　　　色素

matter, carotin, in them. ⑤When you hear the word
　　　カロチン　　　　　　　　　　　　　〜という言葉を聞く

carotin, you may think of carrots or tomatoes. ⑥The
　　　　　　　　　　　　　　　ニンジンやトマト

carotin that shrimp and crab have is similar to that of
　　　　　　　　　　　　　　カニ　　　　〜に似ている

carrots and tomatoes.

⑦The color of the striped pattern of uncooked shrimp is
　　　　　　　　　　　　　　　　　　　　生の（調理されていない）

also that of carotin but it looks blackish, not reddish.

⑧That is because carotin binds with protein. ⑨The carotin
　　　　　　　　　　　　〜と結合する　タンパク質

bound with protein looks dark red or green.
〜と結合した―

⑩When you boil shrimp, the binding between carotin and
　　　　　　　　　　　　　　　　結合

protein comes unbound. ⑪As a result, carotin is back
　　　　　　はずれる　　　　　その結果　　　　　　　　本来の色に戻る

to its original color and shrimp look red.

問62　エビの色は、本当は何色なの？

答 ①魚屋の店頭に並んでいるエビの縞模様は、黒っぽい色をしています。②ところが、食卓に並ぶ、ゆでたエビの縞模様は赤っぽい色をしています。③これは一体、どういうことなのでしょうか？

④ゆでたエビやカニが赤く見えるのは、カロチンという赤い色素を含んでいるからです。⑤カロチンといえば、ニンジンやトマトが思い浮かびます。⑥エビやカニのカロチンは、ニンジンやトマトに含まれるカロチンに近いものです。

⑦生のエビの縞模様もカロチンですが、赤ではなく黒っぽく見えます。⑧なぜなら、カロチンがタンパク質と結合しているからです。⑨タンパク質と結合したカロチンは、暗い赤や緑色になります。

⑩エビをゆでると、熱によってカロチンとタンパク質の結合がはずれます。⑪その結果、カロチンは本来の色に変化し、エビが赤く見えるようになるのです。

What is the difference
between fish with white meat
and fish with red meat?

①Human muscle fibers are made up of red and
人間の　　筋肉繊維　　　　　　〜からなる　　　赤筋

white muscles. ②Red muscle, which has a lot of
白筋

red matter named myoglobin to store oxygen, has
赤い物質　　　　　ミオグロビン　　〜を蓄える　酸素

stamina. ③White muscle, which has instantaneous power
持久力　　　　　　　　　　　　　　　　　　　瞬発力

and can contract quickly, has little staying power and gets
　　　　収縮する

tired soon. ④Human muscles are a mixture of red muscle
　　　　　　　　　　　　　　　　　　　混合したもの

and white muscle, so they look pink.

⑤The difference between fish with white meat and fish
　　〜と一の違い　　　　　　　白身の魚

with red meat is a similar story. ⑥Tuna, mackerel, and
赤身の魚　　　〜に似ている　　　マグロ　　サバ

sardine need to have stamina because they swim long
イワシ　　〜する必要がある　　　　　　　　　　　　　長距離

distances. ⑦That is why they have a lot of myoglobin in

their muscles.

⑧Flounder, sea bream, and so on, which don't swim long
ヒラメ　　鯛

distances, need to get away quickly when they are attacked.
　　　　　　　　逃げる　　　　　　　　　　　攻撃される

⑨That is why their muscles are white and have

instantaneous power.

⑩Horse mackerel are sometimes classified as white meat
　　アジ　　　　　　　　　　　　　　　　　　　　　　　　　　　　　　～に分類される
fish because most of their muscles are white, but they

actually swim long distances and they are red meat fish.
実際には

問63　白身の魚と赤身の魚は、どう違うの？

答 ①人間の筋肉繊維には、赤い色をした赤筋と白い色をした白筋があります。②赤筋はミオグロビンという、酸素を蓄える働きがある赤い物質をたくさん含んでいて、持久力があります。③白筋は瞬発力があって、すばやく収縮しますが、持久力に乏しく、すぐに疲れてしまいます。④人間の筋肉は、この白筋と赤筋が混じっているのでピンク色をしています。

⑤白身の魚と赤身の魚の違いも、これと似ています。⑥マグロやサバ、イワシのように長距離を回遊する魚は、持久力を必要とします。⑦そのため、筋肉にミオグロビンが多く赤身です。⑧ヒラメや鯛のように回遊しない魚は、敵に襲われたときにとっさに逃げる必要があります。⑨そのため、筋肉は瞬発力がある白身です。

⑩アジは、白身が多いため白身魚に分類されることがありますが、実際には回遊魚であり、赤身魚の仲間です。

Why do things burn
when they are set on fire?

①Burning means that something binds with
燃焼　　　　　～を意味する　　　　　　　　～と結合する

oxygen giving off light and heat in an intense
酸素　　　～を放ちながら　　　　　　　　激しく

manner. ②There are a lot of combustible things around us
　　　　　　　　　　　　　　　燃えやすいもの

such as paper, wooden products and cloth. ③However, they
　　　　　　　木製品

do not burn by themselves if you do not set fire to them or
　　　　　　　ひとりでに　　　　　　　　　～に火をつける

heat them. ④Why don't they burn?
～を熱する

⑤Imagine that you move a lighter close to a dry wooden
　～を想像してください　　～を―に近づける　ライター　　　　　乾いた 木の棒

stick. ⑥At first, the surface of the wooden stick becomes
　　　　　　　　　表面

dark brown or black, and then it gradually begins to burn
こげ茶色　　　　　　　　　　　　　　しだいに

with a flame.
炎を上げて

⑦This wooden stick does not burn simply by moving a
　　　　　　　　　　　　　　　　　　　～によってのみでは

fire close to it because cool wood does not have any
　　　　　　　　　　　　冷えた

combustible element in it. ⑧If we heat it with a lighter, the
　　　　　　成分　　　　　　　　　加熱する

element of wood breaks down to become combustible gases
　　　　　　　　分解する　　　　　　　　　可燃性のガス

such as carbon monoxide. ⑨Then, these gases start to burn
　　　　一酸化炭素

with a flame.

⑩Petroleum, gasoline, alcohol, and so on are easier
　石油　　　　　　ガソリン　　　　アルコール　　　　　　　　～よりも燃えやすい
to burn than wood or paper. ⑪These materials release
　　　　　　　　　　　　　　　　　　　　　　　物質　　　　　　放出する
easily combustible gases even though they are not heated.
　　　　　　　　　　　　　　～だとしても

問64　火をつけると、なぜ物が燃えるの？

答　①燃焼とは、物質が激しく光や熱を出しながら酸素と結びつくことです。②私たちの身の周りには紙、木製品、布など、燃えるものがたくさんあります。③にもかかわらず、これらは火をつけたり高温にしたりしないと燃えません。④これは、なぜでしょうか？

⑤ライターの火を乾いた木の棒に近づけるとします。⑥まず、木の表面がこげたような色になり、しだいに炎を上げて燃え始めます。

⑦火を近づけただけでは燃えない理由は、冷えた状態の木には、燃える成分がないからです。⑧ライターの火で熱することにより、木の成分が分解され、一酸化炭素など、可燃性のガスになります。⑨ガスが燃え出すと、炎が上がります。

⑩石油、ガソリン、アルコールなどは、木や紙よりも燃えやすい性質があります。⑪これらは熱せられなくても、蒸発するだけで非常に燃えやすいガスになるからです。

Q65 Why don't pickled plums go bad though they are not dry?

①Food goes bad because of microorganisms such
　　　腐る　　　　　　　　　　　　　微生物

as bacteria. ②Almost all microorganisms cannot
　　細菌

grow without water. ③Therefore people have dried food by
増殖する

sunlight since early times in order to keep the food.
　　　　　　昔から　　　　　　　～するために　　～を保存する

④However, why don't pickled plums go bad even though
　　　　　　　　　　　　梅干し　　　　　　　　にもかかわらず

they contain water?
　　　～を含んでいる

⑤There are two kinds of water in food: bond water and free
　　　　　　　　　　　　　　　　　　　　　　結合水　　　　　　自由水

water. ⑥Bond water binds with the elements of food
　　　　　　　　　　　　～と結合する　　成分

chemically, so it does not evaporate by ordinary way of
化学的に　　　　　　　　　　蒸発する　　　　通常の乾燥法

drying and it does not freeze until around minus 30
　　　　　　　　　　　　凍結する　　摂氏マイナス30度近くまで

degrees C either. ⑦On the other hand, free water binds with

the elements of food loosely, so it can move freely and
　　　　　　　　　　　　ゆるく　　　　　　　自由に動く

evaporate easily. ⑧Microorganisms grow with this free

water and this makes food go bad.

⑨One of the reasons why pickled plums are not likely to
　　　　　　　　　　　　　　　　　　　　　～しにくい

go bad is that they have little free water, and in addition

they are highly <u>acidic</u> and they are salted. ⑩Pickled
　　　　　　　　強い酸性の
plums <u>sold in town</u> sometimes go bad because they do
　　　　町で売られている〜
not have enough salt.

問65　**梅干しは乾燥しているわけでもないのに、
なぜ腐らないの？**

答　①食品が腐るのは、細菌などの微生物によるものです。
②ほとんどの微生物は、水分がないと増えることができません。
③そこで、昔から食品を保存するために、天日に干して乾燥さ
せてきました。④ところが、梅干しには水分が含まれているに
もかかわらず、なぜ腐らないのでしょうか。

⑤食品に含まれる水分には、結合水と自由水の２種類があり
ます。⑥結合水は、食品の成分と化学的に結合しており、通常
の乾燥法では蒸発せず、マイナス30度近くにならないと凍結
もしません。⑦自由水は、食品との結合力が弱く、自由に動く
ことができる水分で、簡単に蒸発します。⑧微生物はこの自由
水によって増殖し、食品を腐敗させます。

⑨梅干しが乾燥していないのに腐りにくい理由には、強い酸と
塩分のほか、この自由水が少ないという理由もあります。⑩市
販の梅干しが腐る場合がありますが、塩分濃度が低く抑えられ
ているためです。

Why water changes to ice
when it is cooled?

①Not only in water but also in any substance,
　　　　　～だけでなく　　　　　～もまた　　いかなる物質において
molecules have the power to pull one another. ②On
分子　　　　　　引く力　　　　　　　互いに
the other hand, they have the power to push each other away
一方　　　　　　　　　　　　　　　　　押す
and try to keep a certain distance when they move
　　　～を維持する　一定の距離　　　　　　　　　近づきすぎる
too close. ③This power is called intermolecular force.
　　　　　　　　　　　　　　　　　　分子間力
④Apart from this, it is the molecule's nature to move
これ以外に
actively when they get energy.
　　　　　　　　　エネルギー
⑤The state of substance can change from gas to liquid, and
状態　　　　　　　　　　　　　　　気体　　液体
then, from liquid to solid according to the balance between
　　　　　　　　固体　　～によって　バランス
the molecular movement and the intermolecular force.
分子の運動
⑥Gas is a state in which molecules have a large amount
　　　　　　　　　　　　　　　　　　　　大量の～
of energy and each of them moves actively and freely.
　　　　　　　　～のそれぞれ　　　　　　　　　　　自由に
⑦Liquid is a state in which molecules pull one another by

the intermolecular force and don't move so actively because

the molecular movement reduces. ⑧Solid is a state in which
　　　　　　　　　　　　減少する
molecules stick close together and move little.
　　　　しっかりとくっつく　　　　ほとんど動かない

172

⑨When you cool water, you take heat energy away
　　　　～を冷やす　　　　　　　　～から－を奪う　熱エネルギー
from the water. ⑩The molecular movement of the water,

which has lost energy, decreases. ⑪Therefore the distance

between molecules becomes small and the molecules stick

close together to become solid by the intermolecular
　　　　　　　結果(～になる)
force. ⑫This state is ice.

問66　水を冷やすと、なぜ氷になるの？

答 ①水に限らず、物質を構成する分子にはお互いに引きつけ合う力が働きます。②一方、近づきすぎると、今度は反発して遠ざけようとする力が働き、一定の間隔を維持しようとします。③「分子間力」と呼ばれる力です。④これとは別に、分子はエネルギーを得ると運動が激しくなる、という性質を持っています。⑤分子の運動と分子間力のバランスによって、物質は気体から液体、液体から固体と形を変えていきます。⑥気体は、分子が大きなエネルギーを持ち、激しく運動してバラバラになっている状態です。⑦液体は分子運動が減少し、分子間力で互いに引き合い、激しく運動しない状態です。⑧そして、固体は分子間力で分子がしっかりくっつき、大きな運動をしない状態です。⑨「水を冷やす」とは、「水から熱エネルギーを奪う」ことです。⑩エネルギーを奪われた水の分子運動は減少します。⑪そのため、分子間の距離も小さくなり、分子間力によって、分子がしっかりとくっついて固体になります。⑫これが氷です。

Q67 Why does it get cold in the refrigerator?

①As noted before, the state of materials changes
　　前に述べたように　　　　状態　　　　物質
from solid to liquid, and then, from liquid to gas
　　固体　　液体　　　　　　　　　　　　　　　気体
according to its energy and the intermolecular force.
～によって　　　　　　　　　　　分子間力
②Pressure is also related to these changes. ③When you put
　圧力　　　　　　～に関係がある
pressure on gas, the intermolecular force is likely to
～に圧力をかける　　　　　　　　　　　　　　　～しやすくなる
work because molecules come close to one another. ④As a
　　　　　　　分子　　　近づく
result, gas change to liquid giving off energy, or heat.
　　　　　　　　　　　　～を出しながら　　　　熱
⑤When you ease pressure on it, the reverse takes place.
　　　　～を弱める　　　　　　　反対のこと　　起こる
⑥That means molecules get cold and changes to gas by
　　つまり　　　　　　　冷たくなる
taking in energy, or heat.
～を取り入れながら
⑦These two theories are applied to the household
　　　　　　　理論　　　～に適用されている　　家庭の
refrigerator. ⑧A material called cooling medium is kept in
冷蔵庫　　　　　　　　　　　冷媒　　　　　～にためられている
the cooling unit of a refrigerator. ⑨When pressure is put on
冷却装置
the cooling medium by a pump that runs on a motor, the
　　　　　　　　　　ポンプ　　　モーターで動く～
state of the cooling medium changes from gas to liquid
giving off heat. ⑩The liquid cooling medium is sprayed
　　　　　　　　　　　　　　　　　　　　　　　～に噴出される

in a low pressure area, so it changes to gas and evaporates.
　　　低圧力　　　　　　　　　　　　　　　　　　　　　蒸発する

⑪It gets cold in the refrigerator because heat is taken away
　　　　　　　　　　　　　　　　　　　　　　　　　　　奪われる

in the process.
その過程で

問67　冷蔵庫はどうして、冷えるの？

答　①物質は、それが持つエネルギーと分子間力によって固体、液体、気体と状態を変えることは、すでに説明したとおりです。

②この変化には圧力も関係します。③気体に大きな圧力がかかると、分子が接近して分子間力が働きやすくなります。④その結果、気体はエネルギー（熱）を出しながら液体になります。⑤液体の圧力を下げると、逆のことが起こります。⑥分子はエネルギー（熱）を使って冷たくなりながら気体になります。

⑦家庭用の電気冷蔵庫は、これら二つの原理を利用したものです。⑧冷蔵庫の冷却装置には、冷媒とよばれる物質が閉じ込められています。⑨モーターで動くポンプで冷媒に圧力をかけると、熱を出しながら気体から液体になります。⑩液体となった冷媒を、圧力が低いところに噴出すると、蒸発して気体となります。⑪このとき熱が奪われるため、冷蔵庫は冷えるのです。

水のエネルギーを奪うと、分子がしっかりくっついて氷になる

When energy is taken away from water, its molecules stick close together and it changes into ice.

水蒸気（気体）
water vapor(gas)

> 分子が大きなエネルギーを持ち、激しく運動してバラバラになっている状態
>
> The state in which molecules have a large amount of energy and each of them move actively and freely

水（液体）
water(liquid)

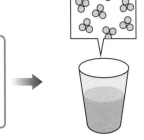

> 分子運動が減少し、分子間力で互いに引き合い、激しく運動しない状態
>
> The state in which molecules pull one another by the intermolecular force and do not move so actively because the molecular movement goes down

氷（固体）
ice(solid)

> 分子間力で分子がしっかりくっつき、大きな運動をしない状態
>
> The state in which molecules stick close together and move little

電気冷蔵庫は、冷媒が気体になるときの気化熱で庫内を冷やす

It gets cold in the refrigerator by the vaporization heat a liquid cooling medium gives off when it changes to gas.

熱を放出
Giving off heat

2

熱を奪う
Taking away heat

液化した冷媒
Devolatilized cooling medium
ディボラティライズド

気化した冷媒
Evaporated cooling medium

1

圧縮機
Compressor

1

気体状態の冷媒は、圧縮機で圧力をかけられ、熱を出しながら液体になる。

Gaseous cooling medium put on pressure by a compressor changes to liquid giving off heat.

2

液体状態の冷媒は、圧力が低いところに噴出し、熱を奪いながら気体になる。

Liquid cooling medium shot up to the place of low pressure changes to gas taking in heat.

How can you see yourself in a mirror?

①There are some things <u>other than</u> a mirror
〜のほかに
which can <u>reflect</u> something. ②Some examples of
〜を映す
these are <u>window glass</u>, <u>still water</u>, and so on.
窓ガラス　　　　　静かな水面
③Things which reflect something <u>have</u> a <u>characteristic</u>
共通して〜を持つ　性質
<u>in common</u>: their <u>surfaces</u> are <u>even</u> and <u>smooth</u>. ④Things
表面　　　　平らな　　ツルツルした
which have this characteristic <u>show</u> <u>specular reflection</u> of
〜を示す　正反射
light. ⑤Specular reflection is a reflection in which <u>light</u>

<u>from a certain direction</u> is <u>reflected</u> <u>at equal angles</u>.
ある方向からの光　　　　反射される　等しい角度で
⑥A <u>well-polished</u> <u>brass plate</u> also shows specular reflection
よく磨かれた　真鍮板
of light but it <u>does not</u> reflect <u>images</u> <u>as clearly as</u> a
像　　　　〜ほどきれいには〜しない
mirror. ⑦A brass plate has a <u>yellowish color</u> because it
黄っぽい色
<u>takes in</u> a <u>bluish color</u>, which is <u>complementary to yellow</u>.
〜を吸収する　青っぽい色　　　　黄色の補色
⑧You may say that polished <u>silver</u> and <u>aluminum</u> have a
銀　　　　　アルミニウム
silver color, but in fact they are <u>colorless</u>. ⑨Colorless
無色
means that they reflect all colors in <u>visible light</u> <u>in the same</u>
可視光線　　　同じように
<u>way</u>. ⑩A mirror, which is made by <u>putting</u> <u>a film</u> of silver
〜を一に貼ること　膜

178

or aluminum on the back of a pane of glass, is colorless.
ガラスの板
⑪It has the characteristic of showing specular reflection of

light without losing any light and you can see yourself in
いかなる光も失うことなく　　　　　　　　鏡で自分自身を見る
the mirror.

問68　　　　　**なぜ、鏡に姿が映るの？**

答　①鏡のほかにも、物体の像が映（うつ）るものがあります。②たとえば、窓ガラス、静かな水面などです。

③像が映りやすいものに共通しているのは、表面が平らで、ツルツルしていることです。④こうした性質のものは光を「正反射」します。⑤正反射とは、入射角と反射角が等しくなる反射のことを指します。

⑥ピカピカに磨（みが）き上げた真鍮板（しんちゅうばん）も光を正反射しますが、鏡ほどきれいに像を映しません。⑦真鍮は、黄っぽい色をしていますが、これは黄色の補色である青っぽい色を吸収しているからです。

⑧磨いた銀やアルミは「銀色」といわれていますが、実はどちらも無色です。⑨無色というのは、可視光線に含まれているすべての色の光を、同じように反射するという意味です。⑩ガラスの裏側に銀やアルミの膜を貼（は）った鏡は無色なのです。⑪それは光を効率よく正反射する性質があるため、きれいに姿を映すのです。

Q69 How does detergent remove dirt?

①It is difficult to <u>remove</u> <u>greasy dirt</u> on <u>plates</u>

落とす　　　油汚れ　　　　皿

with only water. ②Oil and water naturally <u>repel</u>

はじく

each other. ③However, when you use <u>detergent</u>, you can

洗剤

wash away greasy dirt easily. ④This is because <u>the major</u>

洗い落とす　　　　　　　　　　　　　　　　主成分

<u>element</u> of detergent, <u>surfactant</u>, is working. ⑤<u>The</u>

界面活性剤

<u>molecules</u> of the surfactant are like very small <u>matchsticks</u>.

分子　　　　　　　　　　　　　　　　　　マッチ棒

⑥The heads of these "small matchsticks" <u>are likely to</u>

〜しやすい

<u>bind with</u> water and the <u>wood</u> is likely to bind with oil.

〜と結合する　　　　木 [軸]

⑦These "small matchsticks" <u>come between</u> oil and

〜の間に入る

water <u>so that</u> they can bind with each other easily.

〜なので—する

⑧When you use detergent, the part of the surfactant which

can bind with oil first <u>wraps</u> greasy dirt in it. ⑨Many

〜を包み込む

surfactants <u>come close to</u> greasy dirt and they <u>break it</u>

〜にくっつく　　　　　　　　　　　　　　それを〜に分解する

<u>down into</u> small pieces. ⑩<u>Next</u>, water can come between

次に

the greasy dirt and the plate to remove the greasy dirt from

the plate because <u>the outside</u> of the surfactant is likely to

外側

bind with water. ⑪<u>The function</u> that the surfactant

機能

mixes oil and water uniformly in this way is called
均一に　　　このように

<u>イマルシフィケーション</u>
emulsification.
乳化 [作用]

問69　洗剤はどうやって、汚れを落とすの？

答 ①お皿についた油汚れは、水洗いだけではなかなか落ちません。②油と水はなじみにくい性質があるためです。③しかし、洗剤を使うと、油汚れが水できれいに落ちます。④これは、洗剤の主成分である界面活性剤という物質の働きによるためです。⑤界面活性剤の分子はとても小さいマッチ棒のような形をしています。⑥頭の部分は水になじみやすく、棒の部分は油になじみやすい性質があります。⑦これが水と油の境目に入って両方をなじませます。

⑧洗剤を使うと、まず、界面活性剤の油になじむ部分が油汚れを包み込みます。⑨たくさんの界面活性剤がくっついて油汚れを小さく分解します。⑩界面活性剤の外側は水になじみやすい部分なので、汚れとお皿の間に水が入り込んで汚れがお皿から離れていきます。⑪このように界面活性剤が、油と水が均一に混ざった状態にすることを乳化 [作用] といいます。

Q70 Why can erasers erase letters?

①Pencil lead is made by mixing black powder
鉛筆の芯　レッド　　　　～を—と混ぜること

from black lead, with clay and other things, then
黒鉛　　　　　　　粘土

firing it at a high temperature. ②When you rub this on
焼くこと　高温で　　　　　　　　　　こする

paper, the powder from black lead sticks to the surface of
　　　　　　　　　　　　　　　　～にくっつく　表面

the paper because of friction.
　　　　　　摩擦によって

③Some erasers for pencils are made of rubber and
消しゴム　　　　　　～でできている　ゴム

others are made of plastic. ④When you rub this powder
　　　　　　　プラスチック　　　　　～を—でこする

with a rubber eraser, the particles of the black lead on the
　　　　　　　　　　　　粒子

paper stick to the surface of the eraser. ⑤When you keep on

rubbing, these particles and the surface of the eraser
こすり続ける　レジデュウズ

become residue. ⑥Plastic erasers, which are softer than
　　　カス

rubber ones, erase the powder of the black lead on the paper
　　　　　　～を消す

by encasing it.
包み込むこと

⑦It is dificult to erase letters written with ballpoint pens
　　　　　　　　　　　　　　　　　　　　　ボールペン

with an eraser for pencils because the ink sinks into the
　　　　　　　　　　　　　　　　　　　インク　　～にしみ込む

paper. ⑧In this case, we use sand erasers, which are made
　　　　　　　　　　　　　砂消しゴム

of rubber containing fine sand. ⑨They can erase the letters
　　　　　含む　　　細かな

182

written with ballpoint pens by chipping off the surface of

~を削り取ること

the paper which the ink sinks into.

問70　どうして、消しゴムで字が消せるの？

答　①鉛筆の芯は黒鉛という黒い粉を粘土などと混ぜ、高温で焼いたものです。②紙にこすることにより、摩擦で黒鉛の粉が紙の表面に付着します。

③鉛筆用の消しゴムには、ゴム製のものとプラスチック製のものがあります。④ゴム製の消しゴムでこの黒鉛の粉をこすると、紙の表面の黒鉛の粒子がゴムの表面に付着します。⑤さらにこすると、これがゴムの表面とともに消しカスとなります。⑥ゴム製のものよりも柔らかいプラスチック製の消しゴムは、紙の表面の黒鉛の粉を包み込むようにして取り除きます。

⑦ボールペンで書いた文字は、インクが紙にしみ込んでしまっているので、鉛筆用の消しゴムではなかなか消えません。⑧そこで、ゴムに細かい砂を混ぜてつくった「砂消し」を使います。⑨インクがしみ込んでいる紙の表面を砂で削り取ることで、ボールペンの字を消すことができるのです。

Why can an iron
smooth wrinkles?

①Cotton, linen and so on are held together by
綿　　　麻　　　　　　　　結びつけられる
hydrogen bonds caused by the fact that oxygen
水素結合　　　　～によって引き起こされる　　　　　酸素
and hydrogen, which form the molecules of fibers, pull
水素　　　　　　　　　　繊維の分子　　　　　　　～を引く
each other. ②Hydrogen bonds are so weak that they come
　　　　　　　　　　　　とても～なので―　弱い　　　　解ける
undone when they get wet during washing and their
　　　　　　　　　ぬれる　　　　　　洗濯
molecules are broken into pieces. ③When the cloth dries, it
分子　　　ばらばらに分解される　　　　　　　　　乾く
is rough and wrinkled because molecules bind with the
　でこぼこの　シワになった　　　　　　　　　～と結合する
nearest ones, which are different from before.
　　　　　　　　　　　前とは違っている

④Hot steam from irons is good for wool but it cannot
　熱いスチーム　　　　～に適している　ウール
always smooth wrinkles in cotton and linen. ⑤A droplet of
　　　　シワを伸ばす　　　　　　　　　　　　　　水滴
steam is as small as 1/15000th of spray, so it passes
　　　　～の15000分の1と同じくらい小さい　霧吹き　　　　～を通過する
easily through the gaps in fibers. ⑥Therefore the loose
　　　　　　　繊維の隙間　　　　　　　　　　　　　目の粗い
fibers of cotton and linen hardly get wet.
　　　　　　　　　　　ほとんど～しない

⑦By moistening these fabrics not with the steam
　～をぬらすこと　　　　　　　～でではなく―
from irons but with spray, you can easily smooth wrinkles

in cotton and linen . ⑧Bound molecules come undone when
　　　　　　　　　　　結合した

you moisten the cloth. ⑨Ironing at that time makes water
　　　　　　　　　　　　アイロンをかけること
evaporate and the molecules bind with one another again
蒸発する　　　　　　　　　　　　　　互いに
without wrinkles because of the pressure.
　　　　　　　　　　　　　圧力

問71　アイロンをかけると、なぜシワが伸びるの？

答　①綿や麻などは、繊維の分子を構成する酸素と水素が引き合うことから生まれる水素結合で結びついています。②水素結合は弱いので、洗濯して水分を含むことにより解け、分子がばらばらになります。③水分が乾燥するときに、元の結合とは関係なく近くにある分子同士が結合するので、凸凹になり、シワができます。

④ウールには効果的なアイロンのスチーム機能ですが、綿や麻だとシワがよく伸びないことがあります。⑤スチームの水滴は、霧吹きの水滴の 15000 分の 1 というごく小さいもので、繊維の隙間をたやすく通過してしまいます。⑥綿や麻など目の粗い繊維だとほとんど水分が残らないのです。

⑦アイロンのスチーム機能を使わず、霧吹きで水分を与えてやれば、綿や麻でもシワをうまく伸ばすことができます。⑧水分を与えることにより、結合した分子がゆるみます。⑨そこにアイロンをかけることにより水分が気化し、圧力によりシワのない状態で分子が再結合するのです。

洗剤が汚れを落とすのは、水にも油にもなじむから

Detergent removes dirt because it can bind with both water and oil.

洗剤に含まれる界面活性剤の分子
The molecules of the surfactant in detergent

水になじみやすい部分
The part which is likely to bind with water

油になじみやすい部分
The part which is likely to bind with oil

汚れが落ちるしくみ
This is how dirt is removed.

1

界面活性剤が、油になじみやすい部分を汚れの表面にむけて集まる

The part of the surfactant which is likely to bind with oil faces to the surface of dirt.

2

界面活性剤が汚れを包み込む

The surfactant wraps greasy dirt in it.

3

少しずつ汚れを水中に取り出す

Taking dirt away into water little by little.

4

水ですすぐと、汚れは洗い流される

Dirt is removed by flushing with water.

霧を吹いた後、アイロンをかけると、繊維の分子が
きれいに並ぶ

The molecules of fibers line up by ironing after moistening with spray.

凸凹になり、シワが寄った繊維

The fibers which are rough and wrinkled

水素と酸素が不規則に結合している

Hydrogen and oxygen bind with each other disorderly.

シワが伸びるしくみ

This is how wrinkles are smoothed.

霧吹きで水分を与えると、不規則な分子の結合が解ける

When you moistening by spray, disorderly bound molecules come undone.

凸凹がなくなり、シワが伸びた繊維

Smooth fibers which are not rough or wrinkled any more

分子がきれいに並んでいる

The molecules line up.

Q72 Why does a magnet attract iron?

①A magnet attracts metals such as iron, nickel,
<u>磁石</u> <u>〜を引き寄せる</u> <u>金属</u> <u>鉄</u> <u>ニッケル</u>

cobalt, and so on. ②A magnet attracts them
<u>コバルト</u>

because these metals themselves became a magnet for a
<u>それら自体</u> <u>一時的に</u>

time by placing a magnet close to them.
<u>〜を—に近づける</u>

③As you know from the fact that iron becomes an
<u>〜のように</u> <u>〜という事実</u>

electromagnet when you wind nichrome wire around the
<u>電磁石</u> <u>〜を巻く</u> <u>ニクロム線</u>

iron, a magnet has something to do with rotation. ④In the
<u>〜と関係がある</u> <u>回転</u>

molecules of metal, electrons rotate around an electron-
<u>分子</u> <u>電子</u> <u>〜を回転する</u> <u>電子核</u>

shell at the center. ⑤A magnetic force is produced by these
<u>磁力</u>

rotations of the electrons. ⑥However, in the case of most of

the metals, electrons have their pair rotating in the
<u>対になるもの</u> <u>反対方向に</u>

opposite direction and the pairs cancel out each others'
<u>〜を打ち消す</u>

magnetic force. ⑦In the case of iron and other metals, there

are electrons which have no pairs, so a magnetic force is

produced.

⑧However, iron is not usually a magnet. ⑨Imagine that
<u>普通には</u> <u>〜を考えてみなさい</u>

there are countless tiny magnets in iron. ⑩The countless
<u>無数の</u> <u>小さな</u>

magnets are facing in different directions and cancel out
　　　　　むいている　　　いろいろな方向を
the magnetic force of one another. ⑪By placing a magnet

close to them, they face in the same direction and the iron
　　　　　　　　　　同じ方向をむく
becomes a magnet temporarily.
　　　　　　　　　一時的に

問72　なぜ、鉄と磁石はくっつくの？

答　①磁石にくっつく金属は、鉄、ニッケル、コバルトなどです。②磁石を近づけることにより、これらの金属自体が一時的に磁石になるため、磁石にくっつくのです。

③鉄にニクロム線を巻き、電流を流すと電磁石になることからもわかるように、磁石は回転と関係があります。④金属の分子の中では、電子核を中心に電子が回っています。⑤この電子の回転によって、磁力が生まれます。⑥ただし、ほとんどの金属では、逆回りの電子が対になっていて、磁力を打ち消し合います。⑦鉄などでは、対になっていない電子があるため、磁力が生まれるのです。

⑧しかし、鉄は普通の状態では磁石ではありません。⑨鉄の中に小さな磁石が無数にあると考えてみましょう。⑩無数の磁石がばらばらの方向をむき、磁力を打ち消し合っています。⑪磁石を近づけることにより、その向きがそろって一時的に磁石になるのです。

Q73

Why does it become white when light's three primary colors are mixed?

①Visible light, which human beings are able to
可視光線　　　　　　　　　　　　　　　　　　　～できる
see, has many colors in it. ②They are the same
　　　　　　　　　　　　　　　　　　　　　～と同じ—
colors as the many colors from red to purple in the rainbow,
　　　　　　　　　　　　　　　　　　　紫　　　　　虹
which is called the prism in nature.
　　　　　　　　プリズム

③It is human beings that detect colors. ④The retina of the
～するのは—だ　　　　　　　　　　　　　　網膜
eye has three kinds of cone cells: L, M, and S. ⑤Red light
　　　　　　　　　　錐体細胞
excites L cones, green light excites M cones, and blue
～を興奮させる　L錐体
light excites S cones. ⑥Human beings can tell colors
　　　　　　　　　　　　　　　　　　　　　～を見分ける
apart by these three kinds of cone cells. ⑦When these cone
cells get a well-balanced stimulus, human beings
　　　　　　バランスのよい刺激
see it as white.

⑧In other words, the fact is not that it becomes white when
言い換えれば　　　事実は～ではなく—だ
light's three primary colors are mixed but that the color
光の三原色　　　　　　　　　　　混ぜられる
which is made from light's three primary colors is called
　　　～でできている
white. ⑨However, the color white is neutral and is special
　　　　　　　　　　　　　　　　　ニュートラル

for human beings. ⑩This is because white is the most

commonly seen color and it is the color similar to direct
最も普通に見られる〜　　　　　　　　　　　　　　直射日光
sunlight.

問73　光の三原色を合わせると、なぜ白くなるの？

答　①人間の眼で見ることのできる可視光線には、いろいろな色の光が混ざっています。②自然のプリズムといわれる虹の中に見える赤から紫までの色がこれにあたります。

③色を感じとるのは、人間です。④眼の網膜にはL、M、Sの3種類の錐体細胞があります。⑤赤い光はL錐体を、緑の光はM錐体を、青い光はS錐体を刺激します。⑥これら3種類の錐体細胞によって、人間は色を見分けることができるのです。⑦そして、これらがバランスよく刺激されると、人間は白であると感じます。

⑧つまり、「光の三原色を合わせると白くなる」のではなく、「光の三原色を合わせた色を白としている」のです。⑨にもかかわらず、私たちにとって白はニュートラルで特別な色です。⑩なぜなら、白は私たちが一番見慣れた、直射日光に近い色だからです。

Why don't you get burned
in a sauna bath?

①The temperature in a dry sauna bath is very
　　　　　温度　　　　　　　　　乾式のサウナ

high, around 80 to 100 degrees C. ②If you put
　　　　　80～100℃以上　　　　　　　　　　　～に入れる

your finger in boiling water at a temperature higher than 90
　　　　　　　熱湯　　　　　　90度以上の

degrees C, you will get badly burned in no time.
　　　　　　　　　　　　ヤケドする　　　　たちまち

③However, why don't you get burned in a hot sauna bath?

④The first reason is that it is dry in a sauna bath. ⑤When
　　　　　　　　　　　　　　　乾燥した

your body gets hot, you sweat. ⑥In a sauna bath, your body
　　　　　熱くなる　　　汗をかく

secretes sweat because it is dry. ⑦When this happens,
分泌する　　　　　　　　　　　　この過程で

vaporization heat draws the heat from the surface of your
気化熱

body, and at the same time, your body is covered with
　　　　　　　　　　　　　　　　　　　～で覆われる

a cool layer of air.

⑧The second reason is that air doesn't transmit heat as
　　　　　　　　　　　　　　　　～を伝える　　～ほど—しない

well as water. ⑨When you put your finger in boiling water,

its heat is transmitted to your finger directly and you will
　　　　　　　　　　　　　　　　　　直接に

get burned. ⑩However, heat is not transmitted to your body

directly when you take a hot sauna bath naked. ⑪The cool
　　　　　　　　　サウナに入る　　　　　　裸で

layer of air covering your body cuts off heat to some
　　　　　　　　　　　　　　　　　～を遮断する　　　ある程度
extent. ⑫You feel prickling heat when you walk around in a
　　　　　　　　　チクチクする～
sauna bath because the layer of air partly breaks down.
　　　　　　　　　　　　　　　　　　　部分的に壊れる
⑬For these two reasons, you can take a sauna bath at higher

than 90 degrees C for a long time without getting burned.

問74　なぜ、サウナでヤケドしないの？

答　①乾式のサウナの中の気温は 80 〜 100 度以上の高温です。②もしも 90 度以上の熱湯に指を入れたら、たちまち大やけどをしてしまいます。③それなのに、熱いサウナに入ってもヤケドしないのは、なぜでしょうか？

④第 1 の理由は、サウナ内部の湿度が低いことです。⑤体が熱くなると、人間は汗をかきます。⑥湿度が低いため、汗は体の表面で蒸発します。⑦このとき、気化熱として体の表面の熱を奪い、同時に体の表面に温度が低い空気の層ができます。

⑧第 2 の理由は、空気は水に比べて熱を伝えにくいことです。⑨お湯に指を入れると、お湯の熱が直接指に伝わり、ヤケドします。⑩ところが、高温のサウナに裸で入っても、熱は体に直接伝わりません。⑪体の周りにできた、温度が低い空気の層も、熱をある程度遮断してくれます。⑫サウナの中で動くと、チクチクするような熱さを感じるのは、空気の層が乱れるからです。⑬これら二つの理由により、人間は 90 度以上もあるサウナに長時間入っていても、ヤケドすることがないのです。

Why do clock hands move to the right?

①Clock hands move to the right because clocks
　時計の針　　　　　右回りする
were invented in the Northern hemisphere.
　発明された　　　　　　　北半球
②There used to be various clocks such as water clocks, sand
　かつては～があった　　　　　　　　　　　水時計　　　　砂時計
clocks, sundials or sun clocks, and so on before mechanical
　　　　　日時計　　　　　　　　　　　　　　　　機械時計
clocks, which have moving hands, began to be made.

③Among them, sundials were very popular. ④Sundials

tell the hour by the shadow the sun makes. ⑤It is
時を告げる　　　　太陽がつくる影
thought that the shadow moves to the right in the Northern

hemisphere, so mechanical clocks were first made to move

to the right.

⑥Not only mechanical clocks but also almost all
　～だけでなく　　　　　　　　　　　　～もまた
instrument needles move to the right. ⑦It is true that they
計器の針　　　　　　　　　　　　　　確かに～だが，―
were made to move to the right like a clock but moving to

the right like the movement of the sun can be natural for
　　　　　　　　　　　　　　　　　　　　　～でありうる
people living in the Northern hemisphere.

⑧There are quite a few left-handed clocks in the world such
　　　　　少なからず　　　左回りの時計

as the reverse clock in a barber shop, in which clients see
　　　逆回転時計　　　　　　　理髪店　　　　　　　　　客

the clock in a mirror, and watches for special use.
　　　　　鏡に映して　　　　　　　　特別な用途の

⑨However, people have difficulty accepting them partly
　　　　　　　　　　　　　　　　　　　　　　　　　　　　〜だという理由もあって

because they are used to clocks moving to the right
　　　　　　　　　〜に慣れている

in daily life and think they are strange.
日常生活で

問75　時計の針はどうして、右回りなの？

答 ①時計が右回りなのは、時計は北半球で発明されたからです。②現在のように針が回転する機械時計がつくられるようになる前には、水時計、砂時計、日時計といった、さまざまな時計がありました。③なかでも広く使われていた日時計です。④日時計は太陽の影が時間を示します。⑤北半球では影は右回りに動くので、それに合わせて機械時計も右回りにしたのでしょう。

⑥時計に限らず、ほとんどすべての計器の針は右回りです。⑦時計に合わせて右回りにしたというだけでなく、北半球に暮らす私たちにとって、太陽の移動と同じ右回りのほうが、左回りよりも自然なのかもしれません。

⑧理髪店が鏡に映してみるためにつくられた逆回転時計や特殊な腕時計など、左回りの時計も存在しないことはありません。⑨しかし、常日頃から右回りに慣れており、違和感があるためか、ほとんど受け入れられないようです。

鉄の中の小さな磁石の向きがそろうと、鉄は磁石になる

When tiny magnets in iron face in the same direction, the iron becomes a magnet.

鉄
Iron

鉄の中には小さな磁石があり、通常はばらばらの方向をむいている。

There are tiny magnets in iron and they are usually facing in different directions.

磁石を近づけると小さな磁石の向きがそろい、鉄が磁石になる。

When you move a magnet close to them, they face in the same direction and the iron becomes a magnet.

電磁石
Electromagnet

電磁石は、電気の流れにより、小さな磁石の向きがそろう。

In an electromagnet, tiny magnets face in the same direction by a flow of electricity.

サウナでヤケドしないのは、湿度が低いから

You do not get burned in a hot sauna bath because it is dry.

温度は 90 度以上あるが、湿度が低い
The temperature is over 90 degrees C but it is dry.

気化熱が奪われる
Vaporization heat is taken away.

温度の低い空気の層
A cool layer of air

サウナの中は湿度が低いため、汗が盛んに蒸発し、それが体の表面の熱を奪う。同時に冷たい空気が体表に層をつくり、その層が熱をある程度遮断してくれる。
Sweat exudes much from your body because it is dry in a sauna bath and the heat on the surface of your body is taken away. At the same time, a cool layer of air covering your body cuts off heat to some extent.

時計の針が右回りなのは、日時計が右回りだから

Clock was first made to move to the right because the shadow of the sun clock moves to the right.

西　東

南

北半球における日時計の影の動き
The movement of the shadow of the sun clock in the Northern hemisphere

北半球における太陽の動き
The movement of the sun in the Northern hemisphere

北半球では、太陽の移動が右回りに動くので、時計の針も右回りになった
The sun moves to the right in the Northern hemisphere, so clock was first made to move to the right.

Q76 Why does a playback of your recorded voice sound strange?

①When someone else is speaking, his or her real voice and a playback of their recorded
肉声　　　　　　　　　　　　再生　　　　　　　　　　　録音した声

voice sounds similar. ②However, when you record your
～に聞こえる　似ている

voice and play it back, the recorded voice sounds different.
　　　～を再生する

③Why is this?

④A playback of the recorded voice travels through air to your
　　　　　　　　　　　　　　　　　　空気を伝わる

ear, and then it is passed through the outer ear, the middle
　　　　　　　　伝えられる　　　　　　外耳　　　　　　　　中耳

ear, and the inner ear finally reaching the auditory nervous
　　　　　　内耳　　　　　　　　　　　　聴覚神経中枢

center in the cerebrum . ⑤This is called air-transmitted sound.
　　　　　大脳　　　　　　　　　　　　　気導音

⑥When you hear your own voice, it is a mixture of
　　　　　　　　　　　　　　　　　　　　　～と―が混じったもの

air-transmitted sound and bone-transmitted sound which
　　　　　　　　　　　　　骨伝導音

travels through the vocal cords and the skull bone to the
　　　　　　　　声帯　　　　　　　　　頭蓋骨

auditory nervous center. ⑦So your real voice and a

playback of your recorded voice sounds different because of

the difference in the way these sounds travel.
　　　　　　　　　これらの音の伝わり方

⑧The sound from a recorder travels as a air-transmitted
　　　　　　　　レコーダー

sound. ⑨Therefore a playback of your recorded voice
sounds more like your voice that others usually hear.
　　　　　　　 ~のように　　　　　　　　　他人がいつも聞いている~
⑩However, the recorded voice changes a little depending
　　　　　　　　　　　　　　　　　　　　　 ~によって
on the kind of microphone and player. ⑪It is not easy to
　　~の種類　　マイク
hear your own voice as others hear it.
　　　　　　　　　　 ~であるように

問76　どうして、録音した自分の声は変なの？

答 ①他人がしゃべっている場合は、肉声と録音後に再生した声は同じように聞こえます。②自分の声を録音すると、生の声と違って聞こえます。③これは、なぜでしょうか？
④再生された声は、空気を伝わって耳に入り、外耳から中耳、内耳に伝わり、大脳の聴覚神経中枢へたどり着きます。⑤これは気導音と呼ばれています。
⑥自分の声は、声帯から頭蓋骨に伝わり聴覚神経中枢にたどり着く骨伝導音と、気導音がミックスされたものです。⑦このような音の伝わり方の違いから、自分の生の声と再生された声は、違うように聞こえるのです。
⑧レコーダーの音は、気導音として伝わります。⑨したがって、レコーダーで再生されたあなたの声のほうが、いつも他人が聞いているあなたの声に近いことになります。⑩しかし、マイクの種類や再生装置などによって、声が微妙に変わります。⑪他人が聞いているのと同じように自分自身の声を聞くのは、簡単ではないのです。

How are cell-phones connected?

①The cell-phone network is made up of
携帯電話網　　　　　　　　　　　　～から成り立つ
cell-phones you have, base stations, cell-phone
携帯電話　　　　　　　　　基地局　　　　　交換局
switching stations, and the lines between them. ②The base
　　　　　　　　　　　　　　回線
stations are equipment such as antennas which connect to
　　　　　　　　設備　　　　　　　アンテナ　　　　　　　～に接続する
cell-phones wirelessly and they are installed on the roofs
　　　　　　　無線で　　　　　　　　　　設置される
of apartments or other buildings in your town. ③The base

stations are connected to cell-phone switching stations by

optical cable and similar devices.
光ケーブル　　　　　　同様の装置

④Imagine that you turn on your cell-phone. ⑤It
　～を想像してください　　　（～のスイッチを）入れる
connects to a base station and lets the cell-phone
　　　　　　　　　　　　　　　　　　　～に―を知らせる
switching station know which base station's area it is
　　　　　　　　　　　　　　どの～にそれがあるか
in. ⑥The cell-phone switching station records the position
　　　　　　　　　　　　　　　　　　　　　～を記録する　位置情報
information for the base station's area your cell-phone is

in. ⑦When someone calls you, the cell-phone switching
　　　　　　　　　　～に電話する
station finds the nearest base station using the position
　　　　　　　　　　　　　　　　　　　　　　～を使って
information of your cell-phone and calls your cell-phone
　　　　　　　　　　　　　　　　　　　～を呼び出す
by radio waves. ⑧Even if you move to another place
　　　電波　　　　　　～だとしても

within the area of the cell-phone network, you can talk on
　～のエリア内の
the cell-phone because your cell-phone connects to the base

station by itself to update the position information
　　　自動的に　　　　～を更新するために
in the cell-phone switching station. (see p.204)

問77　携帯電話はどうして、つながるの？

答　①携帯電話は私たちの手元にある携帯電話機のほか、基地局、交換局、それらを結ぶ回線によって成り立っています。②基地局というのは電話機と無線でやりとりするためのアンテナを中心とする設備で、マンションやビルなどの屋上に設置されています。③それらは光ケーブルなどにより、交換局と結ばれています。

④あなたが、携帯電話のスイッチを入れたとしましょう。⑤電話機は基地局とやりとりして、どの基地局にいるのかを交換局に伝えます。⑥交換局はあなたの携帯電話がどの基地局のエリアにいるかを、位置情報として記録します。⑦あなたに電話がかかってきた場合、交換局は位置情報から最寄りの基地局を探し、電波であなたの携帯電話を呼び出します。⑧別の場所に移動しても、あなたの携帯電話が自動的に基地局とやりとりして交換局の位置情報を更新するので、携帯電話のエリア内であれば、どこに行っても通話することができるのです。

Q78　How can airplanes fly?

①When you hold a plastic board with the front end slanting upwards and you run, you feel the board move upwards. ②This mechanism is similar to that of flying airplanes.

③When an airplane moves forward, its wings catch the wind. ④The wind which passes over the wings turns downwards a little. ⑤As a result, it puts upward force on the wings. ⑥This causes as a reaction force of downward flow of air. ⑦It becomes a lifting power to lift up the whole airplane.

⑧The wings of the jet airliners today are thicker than before and are curved artfully but the curved lines are different on top than on the bottom. ⑨The lifting force is produced more efficiently by this artful shape of the wings.

(see p.205)

問78　飛行機はなぜ、飛ぶことができるの？

答 ①プラスチックの板を、前方が上になるように傾けて持ち、そのまま走ると、下敷きが上にあがろうとする力を感じるでしょう。②飛行機が飛ぶのも同じようなしくみです。

③飛行機が前に進むと、翼が風を受けます。④翼を通り過ぎた風は、少しだけ下方に向きを変えます。⑤その結果、翼には上向きの力が加わります。⑥下向きの空気の流れの反作用として生まれる力です。⑦これが、飛行機の機体を持ち上げる揚力となります。

⑧現在のジェット旅客機などの翼は厚みがあり、上面と下面が異なる複雑なカーブを描いています。⑨この複雑な形によって、より効率よく揚力が生まれるのです。

どこにいても携帯電話がつながるのは、交換局が すべての電話機の位置を把握しているから

You can talk on the cell-phone anywhere within the area of the cell-phone network because the cell-phone switching station knows where every cell-phone is.

Bさんに発信する
Calling B

交換局に中継する
Hooking up to the cell-phone switching station

Bさんの最寄りの基地局を探し、中継する
Finding the nearest base station to B and hooking up

Aさんの携帯
A's cell-phone

Aさんの最寄りの基地局
The nearest base station to A

交換局
The cell-phone switching station

Bさんを呼び出す
Calling B

Bさんの携帯
B's cell-phone

Bさんの最寄りの基地局
The nearest base station to B

すべての携帯電話がどの基地局のエリアにいるかを、位置情報として常に記録している
Always recording which base station's area every cell-phone is in as the position information.

飛行機は空気の流れを揚力に変えて飛ぶ

Airplanes can fly by changing flow of air to lifting power.

プラスチックの下敷きを、進行方向が少し上になるように傾けて持ち、全速力で走ると下敷きが上にあがろうとする力を感じる

When you hold a plastic board with sloping upwards to its front end and you run as fast as possible, you feel the power of the plastic board to try to move upwards.

上向きの力が働く
Upward force is put on the wings.

下向きの空気の流れの反作用
The reaction force of downward flow of air

飛行機の翼
Airplane wings

空気の流れ
Flow of air

空気が下向きに流れる
Air flows down.

Is it possible to make a time machine?

①It is thought in theory that you can travel from
理論的に　　　　　　　　　　　　　旅する
the present into the future. ②Einstein's special
現在　　　　　未来　　　　　アインシュタインの
theory of relativity is the basis for this and it says that time
特殊相対性理論　　　　　根拠
stops when it moves at the speed of light. ③This means that
光速で移動する
time would stop in a rocket traveling at close to the speed
～するだろう　ロケット　　　　　光速に近い速度で
of light. ④Imagine that a 30-year-old astronaut travels to
～を想像してください　　　　宇宙飛行士　　～を往復する
and from a star about 10 light years away in a rocket
　　　　　　　　　10光年離れた～
at close to the speed of light in 20 years. ⑤The astronaut
　　　　　　　　　　　　20年で
comes back to the earth 20 years later and his classmates in
　　　　　　　　　　　　　　　　　　　学校時代の級友
school are 50 years old at this time but the astronaut is still
　　　　　　　　　このときに　　　　　　　　まだ
30 years old. ⑥This time delay at high speed was already
　　　　　　　時間の遅れ
proven by the fact that clocks run slow in a jet fighter. ⑦It
～によって証明された　　　　遅れる　　ジェット戦闘機
may be possible to make a time machine to travel into
可能である　　　　　タイムマシン　　　　未来へ行く
the future by using this fact.

⑧There are various ideas about a time machine which
　　　　　　　　　　～についての考え
would travel from the present into the past. ⑨However,
　　　　　　　　　　　　　　　　過去

today, most scientists think making it is impossible.
<u>それ(タイムマシン)を作ること</u>　　<u>不可能な</u>

問79　　タイムマシンはつくれるの？

答　①現在から未来への移動は、理論的には可能だと考えられています。②その根拠となるアインシュタインの『特殊相対性理論』では、「光速になると時間は静止する」とされています。③光速に近い速度で飛んでいるロケットがあるとすると、その中の時間は止まっているという意味です。④仮に30歳の宇宙飛行士が10光年離れた星を、20年かけて光速に近い速度のロケットで往復するとします。⑤宇宙飛行士が地球に戻るのは20年後であり、同級生は50歳になっているのに、宇宙飛行士は30歳のままということになります。⑥こうした高速移動時の時間の遅れは、ジェット戦闘機の中の時計が遅れることなどで、すでに証明されています。⑦これを利用すれば、未来へ行くタイムマシンが実現する可能性があります。

⑧現在から過去へ行くタイムマシンについても、さまざまな仮説が立てられています。⑨しかし現在のところ、これは不可能だというのが多数の意見です。

監 修 者

松森靖夫（まつもり　やすお）
1956年神奈川県生まれ。横浜国立大学大学院教育学研究科修士課程修
了。現在、山梨大学教育人間科学部理科教育講座教授。専門は理科教育
学。日本理科教育学会研究奨励賞受賞（1996年）、日本理科教育学会賞受
賞（2000年）。
主な著書には、『論破できるか！子どもの珍説・奇説』（講談社ブルーバック
ス）、『科学　考えもしなかった41の素朴な疑問』（講談社ブルーバックス）、『学
びなおしの天文学（基礎編・応用編）』（恒星社厚生閣）ほか、多数ある。

英 文 監 修 者

Steve Mills（スティーブ　ミルズ）
1961年ワシントン州シアトル生まれ。エンジニア。オリンピックカレ
ッジ在学の後、米海軍原子力学校を卒業。専門の原子力分野だけではな
く、自然科学から物理学まで、科学全般に造詣が深い。

＊本書は書き下ろしオリジナルです。

じっぴコンパクト新書　　375

素朴な「？」がよくわかる！
新版英語対訳で読む科学の疑問
Questions and Answers about Science in Simple English

2020年6月10日　初版第1刷発行

監修者　　**松森靖夫 ＋ Steve Mills**
発行者　　**岩野裕一**
発行所　　**実業之日本社**
　　　　　〒107-0062 東京都港区南青山5-4-30
　　　　　　　　　　　CoSTUME NATIONAL Aoyama Complex 2F
　　　　　電話（編集）03-6809-0452
　　　　　　　（販売）03-6809-0495
　　　　　https://www.j-n.co.jp/
印刷・製本…………大日本印刷株式会社